The geology of the Malin–Hebrides sea area

BRITISH GEOLOGICAL SURVEY

United Kingdom Offshore Regional Report

The geology of the Malin–Hebrides sea area

J A Fyfe, D Long and D Evans
with a contribution by D A Abraham

LONDON HMSO 1993

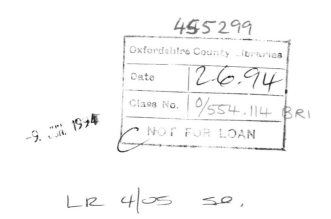

Production of this report was funded by the Department
of Energy and the Natural Environment Research
Council

The coastline used on many maps and diagrams in this book
is based on Ordnance Survey mapping

Bibliographic reference

FYFE, J A, LONG, D, AND EVANS, D . 1993.   *United
Kingdom offshore regional report: the geology of the
Malin–Hebrides sea area.*   (London: HMSO
for the British Geological Survey.)

Dd 295288   C20   3/94

ISBN 0 11 884494 6

Contents

FIGURES

Foreword

The west of Scotland and Northern Ireland have long been important areas in the study of geology, but work on the adjacent seas has been relatively recent. It has become apparent that the offshore geology of the Malin–Hebrides area is significantly different from that of the surrounding land, for there is a much greater proportion of Mesozoic and younger sediments, although the basement rocks that dominate the land continue offshore as important ridges separating the Mesozoic basins. The region was the focus of early Tertiary volcanic activity in the British Isles, when there was emplacement of several basic and ultrabasic intrusions. Erosion of these intrusions has produced offshore placer deposits of chromite and olivine; off Rum, they occur in potentially economic quantities.

Since 1966, the British Geological Survey (BGS) has been studying the area in order to produce a series of maps on a scale of 1:250 000 as part of a survey of the United Kingdom Continental Shelf (see inside back cover). Following the production of these maps, this report has been produced as one of a series of UK Offshore Regional Reports which integrate BGS data and interpretations with commercial information and published material. The area has attracted relatively little interest from the oil industry, so that this part of the UK Continental Shelf has less information on subsurface geology than any other. University groups have nevertheless been active in the area, as has BIRPS (British Institutions Reflection Profiling Syndicate). BGS work during the offshore surveys, and the mapping and report productions phases, has been largely funded by the Department of Energy. I would like to take this opportunity to pay tribute to the long and fruitful co-operation that has existed between BGS and DEn, which has resulted in such major advances in our knowledge of the continental shelf in the Malin–Hebrides area and indeed most other areas of the British continental shelf and margin.

ACKNOWLEDGEMENTS

Responsibilities of individual authors during the production of this report have been as follows:

J A Fyfe — Structure (incorporating a contribution by D A Abraham), Precambrian and Lower Palaeozoic, Devonian, Carboniferous, Permo-Triassic, Jurassic and Cretaceous.

D Long — Quaternary, sea-bed sediments, economic geology and compiler of the report.

D Evans — Introduction and Tertiary; series editor.

The Offshore Regional Report series is co-ordinated by the Marine Geology Group, and edited by D Evans with the assistance of A G Stevenson.

In addition to the work of the authors, the report has drawn extensively upon the knowledge and expertise of other BGS staff, not only within the marine sphere, but also from the Land Survey and specialists in the fields of sedimentology, biostratigraphy, cartography and publication. In particular, much use has been made in this report of palaeontological analyses carried out on borehole material by BGS biostratigraphers. The following are thanked for providing critical comment: M A E Browne, J M Dean, D J Fettes, R J O Hamblin, K Hitchen, A C Morton, S K Monro, J D Peacock, and R J Whittington of University College of Wales, Aberystwyth.

BP Exploration is gratefully thanked for permission to use unreleased data from well 156/17-1 in The Minch, as is the Institute of Earth Studies, UCW, Aberystwyth for allowing us to use the seismic section reproduced in Figure 53.

Peter J Cook, DSc
Director
British Geological Survey

August 1992

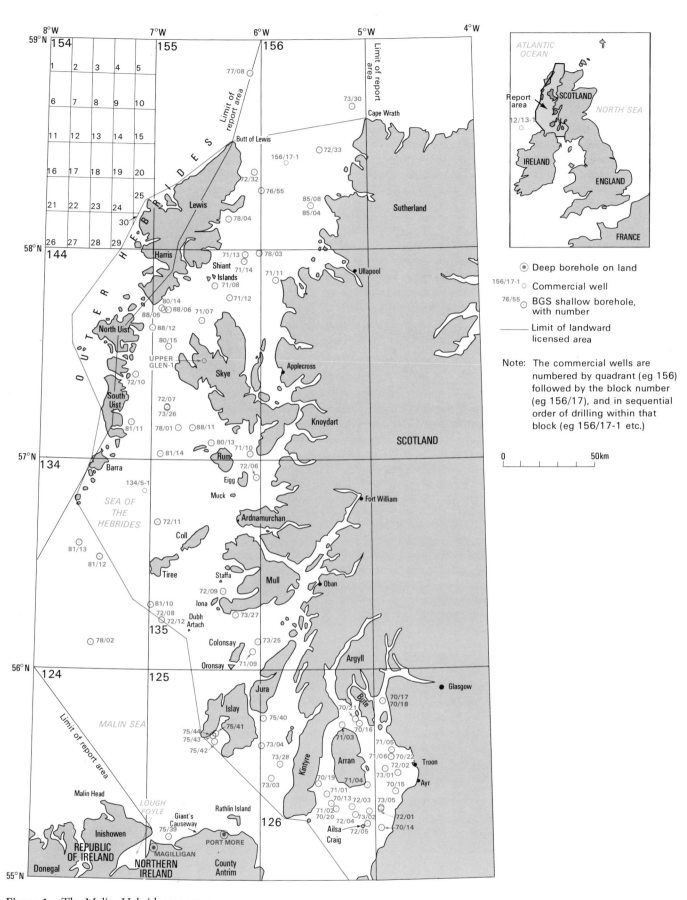

Figure 1   The Malin–Hebrides report area.

1 Introduction

The Malin–Hebrides report area is situated off the west coast of mainland Scotland, and is confined to the inner part of the continental shelf, east of the Outer Hebrides (Figure 1). The sea area covered includes the Firth of Clyde, part of the North Channel, the Malin Sea, the Sea of the Hebrides and The Minch (Figure 2). The area extends northwards from 55°N in the North Channel, and from the north coast of Ireland, to 59°N, north of The Minch. From the Scottish coast the area ranges westwards to the Outer Hebrides in the north and to 8°W farther south. The international boundary between the United Kingdom (UK) and the Republic of Ireland has been agreed to the west of Islay, but not between Lough Foyle and Islay; an arbitrary report area limit has been taken from 56°N 8°W to the mouth of Lough Foyle (Figure 1).

The area is therefore substantially surrounded by land, although much of it remains exposed to the frequent strong winds and near-constant ocean swells which characterise this mid-latitude region. The adjacent land is of variable topography, but is generally rugged and includes many mountains over 1000 m in height. The offshore topography is also very variable, though the relief is of lesser amplitude (Figure 2), with rough ridges separated by smoother, deeper, lows. This pattern is closely related to the offshore geology. The deep water in the Inner Sound east of Raasay is, at 316 m, the deepest recorded on the continental shelf around the UK (McWhirter, 1981).

When interpreting the offshore geology it is generally necessary to extrapolate from the adjacent land, where the geology has been intensively studied since the early 19th century. Work offshore has only been in progress since the late 1960s.

Precambrian to Early Palaeozoic metamorphic rocks are particularly abundant around the coast, and include extensively outcropping Lewisian gneisses, the oldest rocks in the UK. These gneisses make up the Outer Hebrides and much of north-west Scotland, as well as cropping out at several other localities on the western side of Scotland (Figure 3) where they produce rough topography, although not necessarily with great relief. Offshore, these rocks form ridges or highs with a rough sea bed, and within the report area, have their most extensive outcrop at the Stanton Banks. Moine and Dalradian metamorphic rocks of largely Precambrian age form mountainous terrain on land, and can be traced offshore as ridges such as the Middle Bank between Islay and Inishowen (Figures 3 and 4). Unmetamorphosed Precambrian Torridonian sandstones form spectacular isolated hills in Sutherland, and also tend to form rugged topography offshore, particularly in the Hawes Bank area (Figures 2 and 3).

A ribbon of Cambro-Ordovician sediments crops out from Loch Eriboll to Skye, but are unproven offshore. Ordovician to Silurian rocks are present in the extreme south-east of the report area, around the Southern Upland Fault (see Figure 4). Devonian and Carboniferous rocks do not occur widely either onshore or offshore, although they are common in the Firth of Clyde region, where the Midland Valley Graben of Scotland extends south-westwards.

The most significant difference between the geology of the Scottish landmass and the submarine geology off its west coast is that a large area offshore is underlain by Permian and Mesozoic rocks. A number of sedimentary basins form the lower-lying and generally smoother zones between ridges of older rock. These younger rocks crop out only sporadically on land, and occur extensively only where they have been protected from erosion by the presence of thick basalts, notably in Antrim and on Skye. These two areas are geologically more closely related to the offshore region than to the land.

The largest sedimentary basin is the Sea of the Hebrides–Little Minch Trough, which extends from the Stanton Banks northwards to the Rubha Reidh Ridge, and includes the well-documented Jurassic sediments exposed on Skye (see Figure 4). To the north lies the North Minch Basin, and several smaller troughs have been identified to the south-east. Permo-Triassic basins cover much of the Firth of Clyde and North Channel.

The basins are commonly bounded by faults that were initiated during the Caledonian orogeny or earlier, and reactivated during and after the Permo-Triassic as normal faults. Important dislocations that extend both onshore and offshore include the Great Glen, Highland Boundary, Tow Valley and Loch Gruinart faults (Figure 4). The Minch Fault does not extend on to land, but its existence was originally postulated from supposed displacement of Lewisian rocks on either side of The Minch (Dearnley, 1962).

Parts of the west coast of Scotland and Northern Ireland have become classic areas for the study of Tertiary volcanicity (Richey, 1961; Preston, 1981). Volcanic centres such as the Cuillins of Skye and the Central Complex of Arran form mountainous regions onshore, and the Blackstones Bank igneous centre has been discovered offshore where it forms a rugged area of sea bed (McQuillin et al., 1975). The well-known basalts of Skye, the Giant's Causeway in Antrim, Mull, and Fingal's Cave on Staffa have been traced offshore where they form predominantly flat-topped plateau areas (Figures 1 and 3). In addition to the early Tertiary igneous rocks, basins of Oligocene sediments have been discovered in the report area; these are considered to be comparable to the deposits at Lough Neagh to the south of County Antrim.

The topography of the report area was greatly modified by the Quaternary ice sheets which strongly eroded the weaker Mesozoic sediments in preference to metamorphic and igneous rock types, resulting in substantial overdeepening of the sedimentary basins. Many of these basins have since been partly filled with a considerable thickness of Quaternary sediments, providing a smooth, deep, sea bed that tends to be muddier than the higher areas which are generally covered by sands and gravels. Present-day sedimentation is greatly affected by the tidal streams which are often strong, particularly in the North Channel where they have swept away any Quaternary sediment to leave Permo-Triassic rocks at the sea bed.

HISTORY OF RESEARCH

Study of offshore geology is a comparatively recent topic of research, and few projects anywhere predate the Second World War; the present area and surrounding regions are no exception. In the early part of this century, Cole and Crook (1910) described varied rock specimens dredged from the sea floor around Ireland, but not until the late 1960s did work begin in earnest by the Institute of Geological Sciences (now the British Geological Survey — BGS), UK universities and other groups including oil companies. In 1966, the first BGS

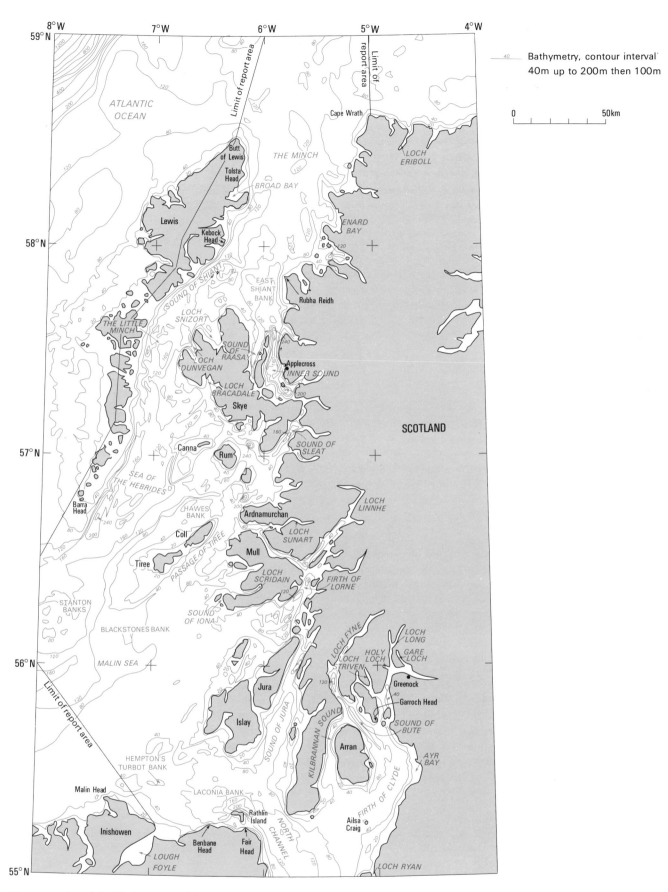

Figure 2 Simplified bathymetry of the report area.

offshore project (Fannin, 1989) was a small geophysical study of the Minch Magnetic Anomaly, a feature already identified from the BGS aeromagnetic survey of the UK (see Figure 6). In the late 1960s, marine geophysical surveys by BGS in the Firth of Clyde, Sea of the Hebrides and The Minch indicated the presence of offshore sedimentary basins. At that time, workers at Glasgow University were also beginning geophysical work in the Firth of Clyde and in the Little Minch (McLean et al., 1970; Smythe et al., 1972), and BGS had the opportunity to use the manned submersible *Pisces* to observe the sea floor and collect samples (Eden et al., 1971; 1973).

In the early 1970s, BGS carried out a shallow drilling programme over much of the UK Continental Shelf employing the drilling ship *mv Whitethorn* (Chesher et al., 1972; Evans et al., 1982). This project proved extensive Mesozoic rocks offshore in the Malin–Hebrides area. BGS geophysical and sampling surveys continued, and workers at University College London and the University College of Wales (UCW) Aberystwyth also began projects in the area, producing papers on the Sea of the Hebrides (McQuillin and Binns, 1973), the Blackstones Bank igneous centre (Faruquee, 1972), the Malin Sea (Dobson and Evans, 1974) and The Minch (Smythe et al., 1972; Bishop and Jones, 1979). Over the same period, workers at Durham and elsewhere were carrying out refraction experiments to study the deeper crustal geology (Smith and Bott, 1975; Bott et al., 1979).

After the broad pattern of the geology had been established, specific studies were carried out on such features as the Blackstones Bank igneous centre and the Islay–Jura dyke swarm (Durant et al., 1976; Barber et al., 1979). The area also attracted the attention of the French workers Gerard and Boillot (1977), who produced a paper on the geology and structure of the Malin Sea.

While most attention was being focused on the solid geology, there was also interest in the Quaternary geology and sea-bed sediments. Binns et al. (1974a) presented a Quaternary stratigraphy for the Sea of the Hebrides, and this scheme was radically revised following the work of Davies et al. (1984). Pendlebury and Dobson (1976) outlined the nature of recent sediments of the Malin Sea, and

Deegan et al. (1973) described the sea-bed deposits of the Firth of Clyde.

In 1981, the British Institutions Reflection Profiling Syndicate (BIRPS) ran their first seismic line, the Moine and Outer Isles Seismic Traverse (MOIST), off the north coast of Scotland, crossing the northern part of the report area (see Figure 7). This profile collected data from 15 seconds two-way travel time and was designed to study the structure of the deep crust, the Moho and the upper mantle (Smythe et al., 1982; Brewer and Smythe, 1984). Later, other BIRPS profiles, WINCH (Western Isles and North Channel) and WIRE (West of Ireland), were run through the southern part of the area (Hall et al., 1984; Klemperer et al., 1991).

The hydrocarbon industry showed a generally low level of interest in the area during the 1970s, when many oil and gas discoveries were being made in the northern North Sea and drilling was being carried out in the Irish sector. Some seismic-reflection surveys were run at this time, but not until the 1980s were any UK landward area licences granted for oil exploration in the Sea of the Hebrides, the Firth of Clyde and on Skye. Earlier, licences had been granted around Rathlin Island under a separate arrangement. The first offshore well in the area was drilled in The Minch (Figure 1) by BP in the summer of 1989, although land rigs had operated earlier in Northern Ireland and northern Skye. The dearth of available information from the oil industry has meant that neither the structures nor the geological successions of the sedimentary basins are as well known as in most areas around the UK.

In the 1980s, BGS completed their reconnaissance surveys and began producing 1:250 000 scale maps of the solid geology, Quaternary geology, sea-bed sediments, Bouguer gravity anomalies and aeromagnetic anomalies (see index map inside the back cover). This was in several instances carried out in conjunction with university groups, most notably UCW Aberystwyth. These maps are based on all available data collected in the area; BGS alone have collected some 30 000 km of geophysical traverses, 1300 sea-bed samples and 75 shallow boreholes. These data and their interpretations, combined with other published or available data, are used in the production of this UK Offshore Regional Report.

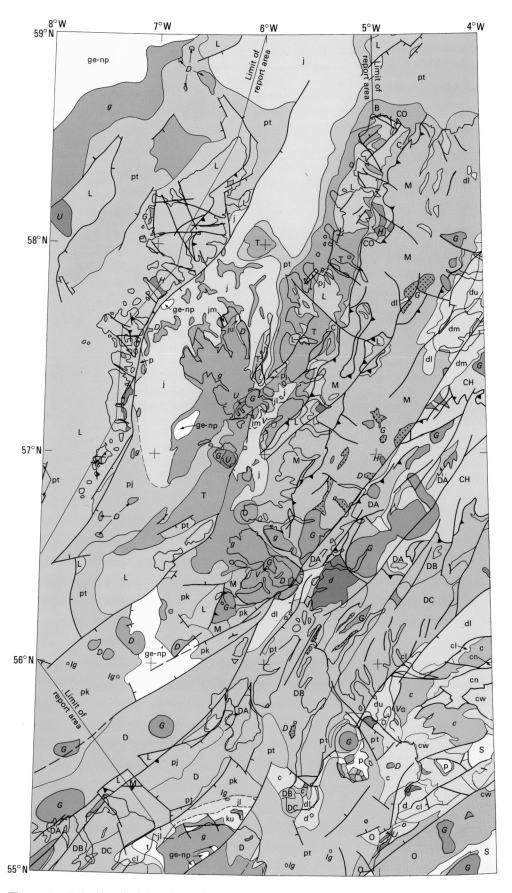

Figure 3 Generalised solid geology of the report area

4

KEY

SEDIMENTARY ROCKS

| ge-np | Eocene-Pliocene | } Tertiary |

| ku | | } Upper Cretaceous |

| j | ju Upper / jm Middle / jl Lower | } Jurassic |

| t | | } Triassic |

| pt | pk Permian-Cretaceous / pj Permian-Jurassic | } Permo-Triassic (or younger) |

| p | | } Permian |

| c | cw Westphalian / cn Namurian / cl Dinantian | } Carboniferous |

| d | du Upper / dm Middle / dl Lower | } Devonian |

| S | | } Silurian |

| O | | } Ordovician |

| CO | | } Cambro-Ordovician |

| C | | } Cambrian |

| T | Torridonian | } Precambrian |

0   50km

METAMORPHIC ROCKS

| D | DC Upper / DB Middle / DA Lower | } Dalradian |

| CH | | } Central Highland Division and Grampian Group |

| M | | } Moine |

| L | | } Lewisian (including Islay Terrane) |

| B | | } Undivided |

IGNEOUS ROCKS

Extrusive

g	Palaeogene
c	Carboniferous and Permian
d	Devonian
o	Ordovician

Intrusive

G	Acid
H	Intermediate
D	Basic
U	Ultrabasic
V	Vent agglomerate

| lg | Igneous, undivided |

Metamorphosed igneous rock

——— Geological boundary, dashed where uncertain

—⊥— Fault at surface; crossmark on downthrow side

– ⊥ – Fault at depth

—▲— Thrust, slide or shear zone.

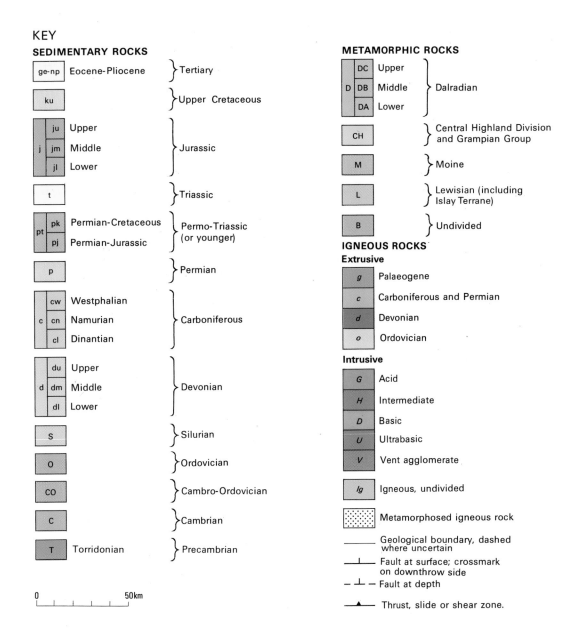

5

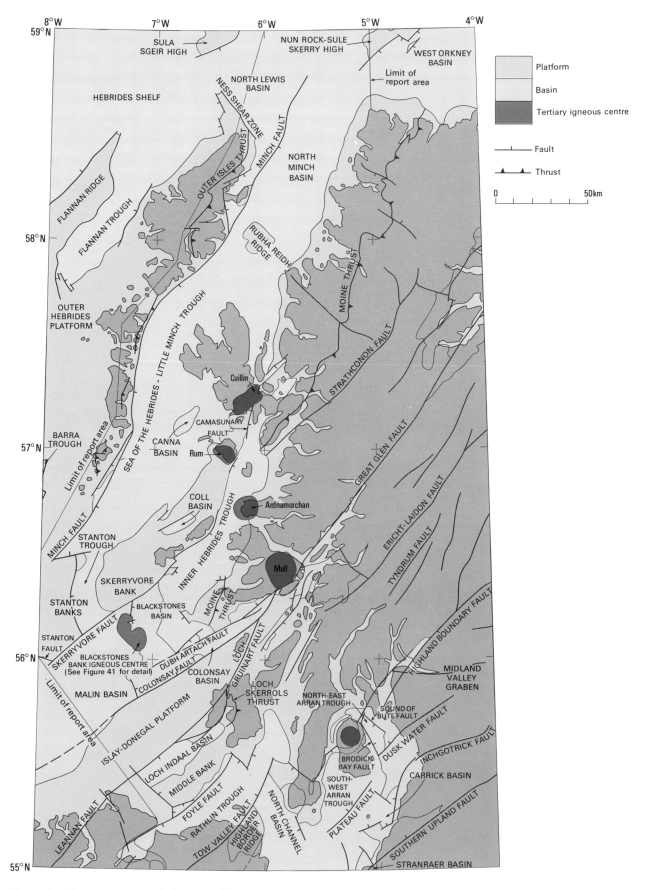

Figure 4 The main structural elements of the Malin–Hebrides area.

2 Structure

The Malin–Hebrides area is traversed by a series of major, ancient structural dislocations that date back to the Caledonian orogeny and beyond. They include the Outer Isles and Moine thrust zones, the Great Glen Fault and associated faults, and the Highland Boundary and Southern Upland faults (Figure 4). Some of these major faults, such as the Moine Thrust and the Great Glen Fault, have been shown to affect the Mohorovičić Discontinuity (Moho) at the base of the crust. These structures commonly separate regions of differing geological character, and Late Palaeozoic to Mesozoic basins are largely bounded by them, following their reactivation during basin formation. The initiation of this later basin development may perhaps have been associated with early rifting in the North Atlantic during the Carboniferous. Sedimentation within these basins was particularly active during the Permo-Triassic, and then continued during the Jurassic and perhaps into the Early Cretaceous. Younger Tertiary basins were formed at a time of more regional subsidence, although some of the bounding faults were active through to at least mid-Tertiary times.

STRUCTURAL FRAMEWORK

The major structural features in the Malin–Hebrides area may be identified from the pattern exhibited by Bouguer gravity anomalies (Figure 5). The two most significant characteristics shown by the Bouguer gravity-anomaly map are the strong, linear contours which define the margins of areas of low gravity anomaly values associated with the sedimentary basins, and the closely spaced, largely circular contours describing positive gravity anomalies related to Tertiary igneous centres. The use of aeromagnetic anomaly data for structural interpretation is partly limited by the masking effect of the widespread near-surface igneous rocks, but the smooth contours over the North Minch and North Channel basins and parts of the Sea of the Hebrides–Little Minch Trough confirm the presence of a thick, nonmagnetic, sedimentary sequence (Figure 6; BGS Aeromagnetic Anomaly sheets).

In the north-west of the area, the long, sinuous, gravity anomaly expression of the Minch Fault, and the adjacent thick sediments to the east, can be traced over a distance of some 200 km. In the north, high gravity anomaly values associated with the basement areas of the Outer Hebrides and the Scottish mainland contrast with the lower values over the intervening North Minch Basin. Within the basin, the linear, negative, Minch aeromagnetic anomaly (Figure 6) contrasts with the generally smooth background contour pattern; this anomaly has been interpreted as a major Tertiary dyke (Ofoegbu and Bott, 1985). The North Minch Basin is a westerly dipping half-graben bounded to the west by the Minch Fault, as is the Sea of the Hebrides–Little Minch Trough from which it is separated by the Rubha Reidh Ridge. To the south-west of Skye, a low Bouguer gravity anomaly is centred on the Canna Basin, a sub-basin of the Sea of the Hebrides–Little Minch Trough (Figure 4) that contains Oligocene sediments.

The intense aeromagnetic signature over Skye (Figure 6 and see Figure 38) defines the limit of the extrusive rocks over much of the island, and this anomaly pattern extends south-westwards over the basalts, including the part that forms the downwarped floor of the Canna Basin. A distinctive magnetic anomaly pattern occurs over the basalts and other extrusive rocks which crop out over most of Mull and extend westwards to the Lewisian of Coll (BGS Tiree Aeromagnetic map; Figure 6). These basalts partially cover the Permian to Mesozoic rocks of the Inner Hebrides Trough, a half-graben which is largely bounded to the west by the north-easterly trending Skerryvore Fault, although to the south of Skye it is bounded by the north–south-trending Camasunary Fault (Figure 4). In the south, the largest area of high gravity anomaly is that associated with the Lewisian of the Skerryvore Bank to the north-west of the Skerryvore Fault. Adjacent to the Skerryvore Bank lies the Blackstones Basin, a sub-basin at the southern end of the Inner Hebrides Trough in which sediments of probable Oligocene age are preserved.

In the south-west of the area, another high Bouguer gravity anomaly is coincident with the Stanton Banks (Figures 4, 5 and 18), which are separated from the Skerryvore Bank by the Stanton Trough. The Lewisian of Skerryvore Bank and the Stanton Banks are both characterised by intense aeromagnetic anomalies (BGS Tiree Aeromagnetic map; Figure 6). The Stanton Banks are also bounded to the south-east by the Skerryvore Fault, which separates them from the Malin Basin to the south. The Malin Basin is separated from the Inner Hebrides Trough by the Tertiary Blackstones Bank igneous centre, which produces the most prominent high gravity anomaly value in the report area (Figure 5).

To the south of Mull, the Colonsay Basin is a graben that extends along the line of the Great Glen and associated faults. Low gravity anomaly values are associated with this basin, which is bounded to the south-east by the Colonsay Fault.

The Colonsay Fault defines the north-western boundary of much of the Islay–Donegal Platform (Figure 4), to the south-east of which fault-bounded, or partly fault-bounded structures such as the Rathlin Trough and the Loch Indaal Basin are marked by significant elongate Bouguer gravity anomaly lows. The Loch Indaal Basin is a half-graben, filled with Permian to Jurassic sediment. It developed to the south-east of the Loch Gruinart Fault, which extends north-eastwards towards the Great Glen Fault and south-westwards to the Leannan Fault (Dobson et al., 1975). The Rathlin Trough is bounded by the extensions of the Foyle and Tow Valley faults, both of which may be related to large Caledonian dislocations in Scotland (Pitcher, 1969; Evans et al., 1980).

A low gravity anomaly occurs over the north-westerly trending Permo-Triassic North Channel Basin. This basin is joined at the surface to the South-West Arran Trough (Figures 3 and 4). Although the Highland Boundary Fault is a conspicuous feature marking the north-western limit of the Midland Valley Graben in mainland Scotland, it has not been traced either onshore or offshore to the south-west of Arran. The Southern Upland Fault is an important dislocation whose likely position offshore in the North Channel is apparent from

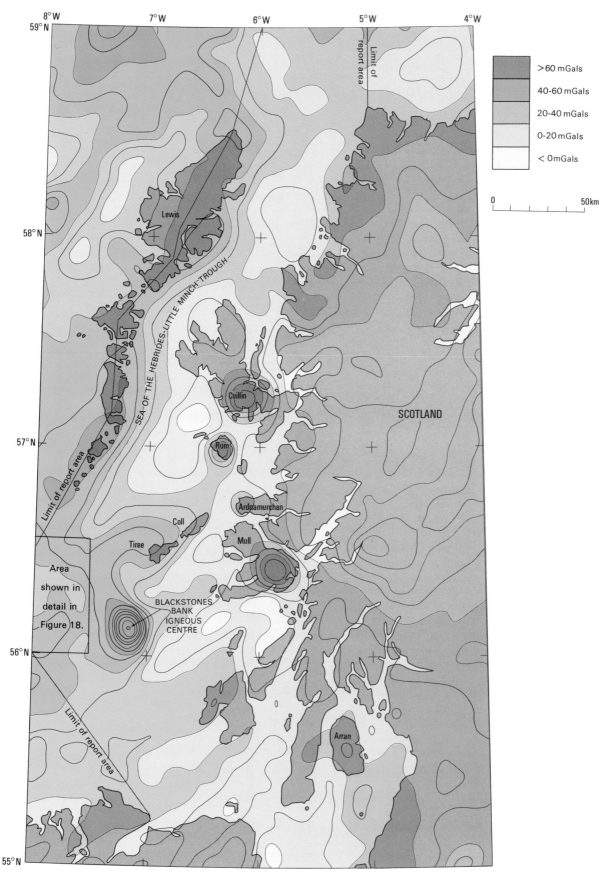

Figure 5 Bouguer gravity anomaly map.

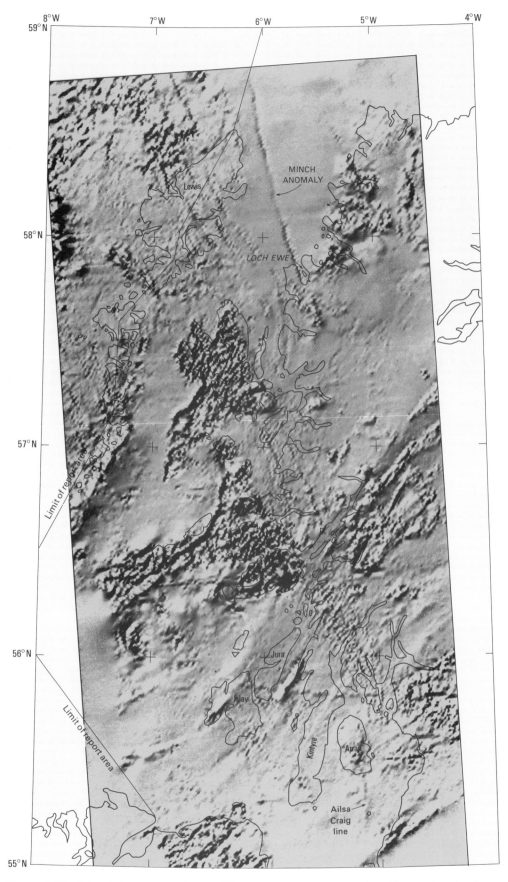

Figure 6 Shaded-relief aeromagnetic map. The map was computer produced by treating the data as a topographic relief surface illuminated from the north-west at an angle of 30°. The northernmost part of the report area is not shown.

9

Figure 7 The locations of deep-seismic reflection and seismic-refraction lines in relation to some major structural features.

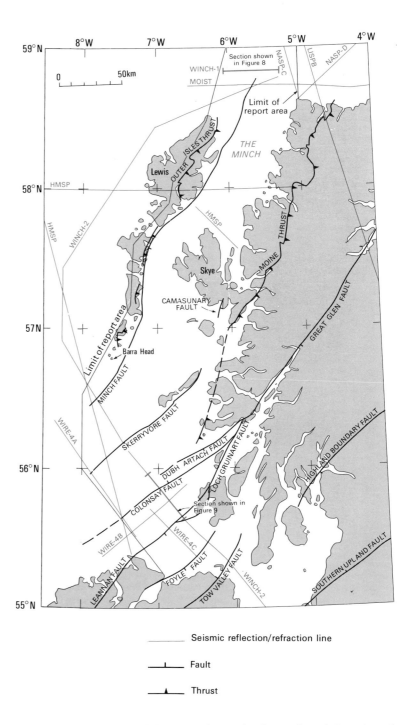

Seismic reflection/refraction line

━━┴━━ Fault

━━▲━━ Thrust

the aeromagnetic field, although it is not recognised seismically (Hall et al., 1984; BGS Isle of Man Solid Geology sheet).

CRUSTAL STRUCTURE

Amongst early seismic refraction data collected in order to discover the nature of the crust off north and west Scotland (Figure 7) was that obtained by two experiments: the North Atlantic Seismic Project — NASP (Smith and Bott, 1975) and the Hebridean Margin Seismic Project — HMSP (Bott et al., 1979). Subsequently, deep-seismic reflection data (Figure 7) were collected over the area by BIRPS (McGeary et al., 1987). However, correlation between the results of the two seismic methods is not necessarily good; McGeary et al. (1987, p.37) compared BIRPS results with those of the LISPB refraction study across mainland Scotland (Bamford et al., 1978), and concluded that 'no systematic variation in reflectivity can be tied either to tectonic provinces or seismic refraction layers or velocities'.

North of the Scottish mainland, Smith and Bott (1975) showed a two-layered crust, with the Moho at a depth of some 26 km. This was confirmed by the BIRPS' MOIST line that gave an almost continuous Moho reflection at about 25 km (Smythe et al., 1982). The HMSP showed the continental crust beneath the Hebridean shelf west of Lewis to be about 27 km thick, deepening eastwards to some 28 km to the north of Skye (Bott et al., 1979). From the WINCH reflection-seismic line, the Moho can be identified as a subhorizontal surface at 30 km depth near the Great Glen fault zone, shallowing to 25 km beneath the Loch Indaal Basin. The BIRPS' WIRE lines show the depth of the Moho south of Islay to be around 28 km (Klemperer et al., 1991). A depth of some 32 km was identified beneath the Firth of Clyde (Hall et al., 1984), similar to that calculated beneath the Midland Valley by Bamford et al. (1978).

McGeary et al. (1987) described a 'Typical BIRP' profile from BIRPS sections collected around the UK. This idealised profile consists of a strongly reflective upper crust, which is commonly equated with Mesozoic basins, overlying a relative-

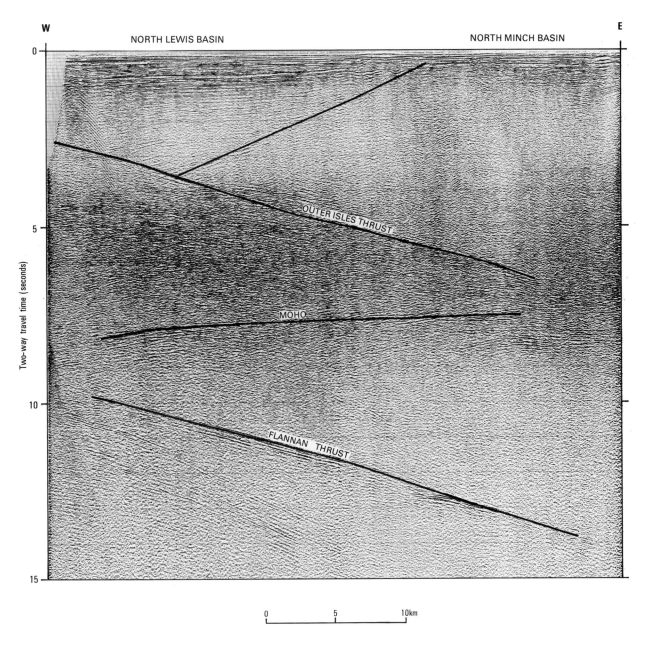

W NORTH LEWIS BASIN NORTH MINCH BASIN E

OUTER ISLES THRUST

MOHO

FLANNAN THRUST

Two-way travel time (seconds)

0 5 10km

Figure 8 The BIRPS WINCH-1 seismic-reflection section north of The Minch, showing the interpretation of Brewer et al. (1983). For location see Figure 7.

ly nonreflective middle crust which is locally cut by major dipping reflectors. Beneath this is a strongly subhorizontally layered lower crust over a clearly defined Moho which marks the top of the unreflective mantle. In some cases the Moho is crossed by dipping reflectors. To north of The Minch, BIRPS lines correspond well with this idealised profile (Figure 8); prominent dipping reflectors in the middle crust represent the Outer Isles Thrust, and in the mantle beneath the Moho, a prominent dipping reflector has been identified as the Flannan Thrust, a structure not identified from the surface geology (Smythe et al., 1982; Brewer and Smythe, 1984; 1986).

The deep structure of the Outer Isles Thrust to the north of Lewis has been interpreted from commercial seismic-reflection data as extending from the surface to the mid-crust (Brewer and Smythe, 1986; Stein, 1988). It has been interpreted as showing earliest movement in the Proterozoic, with only minimal Caledonian displacement (Lailey et al., 1989), but suffering post-Caledonian normal reactivation from Carboniferous to Tertiary times. Stein (1988) proposed that this reactivation was associated with en-échelon movement on the Minch Fault.

No BIRPS information is available for the region east of the Outer Hebrides, where Bott et al. (1979) showed the crust as a single unit of 6.4 km/s velocity, but interpretation of the WINCH line to the south of Barra Head by Hall et al. (1984) shows a reflective lower crust bounded below by the Moho and associated with a number of dipping 'thrusts'. Lower crustal layering is clearly seen both north-west of the Skerryvore Fault and south-east of the Great Glen Fault, but the central portion between these faults appears as a blank zone. Snyder and Flack (1990) attributed this blank zone not only to change in lower crustal geology, but also to the disruptive effect on the seismic signal of fault zone structures close to the surface.

Brewer et al. (1983) speculated that southerly dipping reflectors between 30 and 40 km depth to the south of the Great Glen Fault represent the Flannan Thrust south of the Outer Hebrides (Figure 9). Given that these reflectors are truncated by the Great Glen Fault and are absent to the north, Brewer et al. (1983) postulated a left-lateral offset of between 100 and 150 km along the fault.

On the WINCH profile, the Dubh Artach Fault defines the north-western boundary of the Colonsay Basin (Figure

11

COLONSAY BASIN

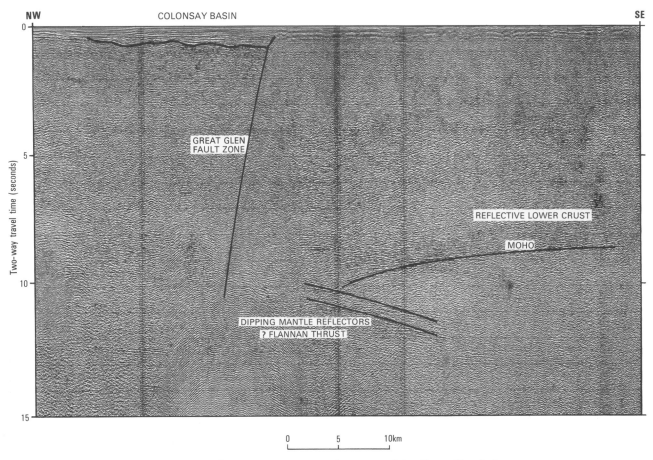

Figure 9 Part of the BIRPS WINCH-2 deep-seismic section in the region of the Great Glen fault zone. Interpretation adapted from Hall et al. (1984). For location see Figure 7.

4). The throw on this fault becomes more pronounced with depth, and it dips steeply to the south-east to merge with the Great Glen Fault. Farther south-east, the Loch Gruinart Fault is interpreted as a twice-reactivated splay of the Great Glen Fault (Evans et al., 1982; Hall et al., 1984). Hall et al. (1984) interpreted the Loch Gruinart Fault as rooting into a thrust deeper than the Loch Skerrols Thrust, and taken to be the continuation of the Moine Thrust south of the Great Glen Fault (Fitches and Maltman, 1984). In the North Channel, BIRPS profiles do not reveal either the Highland Boundary or Southern Upland faults (Hall et al., 1984), despite both being considered by Hutton (1987) as terrane boundaries.

STRUCTURAL EVOLUTION

The Phanerozoic structural evolution of the Malin–Hebrides area can be related to two major episodes of plate tectonic movement: the closing of the Iapetus Ocean in the Early Palaeozoic which drove the Caledonian orogeny, and the later opening of both the North Atlantic Ocean and the north-east Atlantic Ocean.

The closing of the Iapetus Ocean involved the northerly subduction of oceanic crust beneath the margins of the ancient Laurentian continent which lay to the north-west of that ocean (Ziegler, 1981; Leggett et al., 1983; Chadwick and Holliday, 1991). This ocean closure led to the joining of Laurentia, which included southern Scotland and the north of Ireland, with Avalonia, which included the rest of the British Isles. This formed the supercontinent of Pangaea. The Caledonian foreland in the north-west of the report area formed a largely stable area unaffected by Caledonian folding

(Ziegler, 1981), with the Moine Thrust, the Caledonian front, effectively marking the south-eastern margin of this craton. Thrusts to the west, such as the Outer Isles Thrust, may be reactivated Proterozoic structures (Stein, 1988; Fettes et al., 1992). Within the Great Glen fault complex, wedges of Lower Devonian sediments and lavas which postdate the main movement show deformation which suggests active contemporaneous tectonism within the fault zone (Stoker, 1982). These major Caledonian faults have a generally northeast to south-west trend, and define the structural framework for the report area.

Johnson et al. (1979) divide the Scottish Caledonides into an orthotectonic zone north of the Highland Boundary Fault, and to the south a paratectonic zone that comprises the Southern Uplands and the Ballantrae Complex (Figure 10). Within the orthotectonic zone, deformation resulted mainly from polyphase nappe development and thrust tectonics. Deformation in the paratectonic zone is mainly associated with listric faulting, the development of the accretionary prism, and thrust tectonics (Stone et al., 1987).

The orthotectonic zone is in turn divided into a northern part between the Moine Thrust and the Great Glen Fault, and a southern part between the Great Glen and Highland Boundary faults. Metamorphic rocks to the north of the Great Glen were affected by Caledonian (440 Ma) and late Proterozoic (c.750 Ma and possibly c.1000 Ma) phases of deformation (Fettes and Harris, 1986). At the present level of exposure, the southern part was mainly affected by the Grampian tectonothermal event at around 490 Ma, with evidence for earlier deformation and metamorphism at about 590 Ma (Rogers et al., 1989). The pre-Appin Group rocks show evidence of a possible c.750 Ma event (Piasecki and van Breeman, 1983).

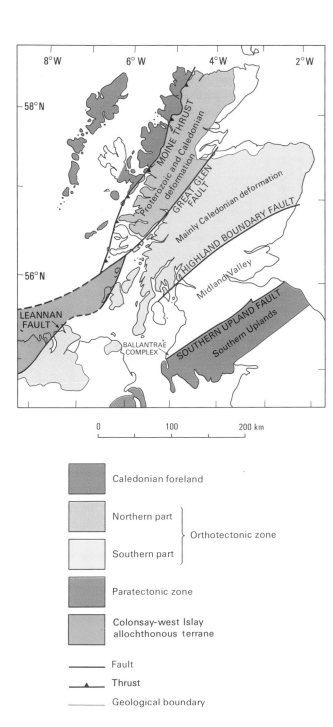

Figure 10 Generalised divisions of the Caledonides of Scotland and Northern Ireland. Based on Johnson et al. (1979) and Fitches et al. (1990).

Both syn- and postorogenic granites were emplaced, and Early Devonian lavas occur in the Firth of Lorne.

During the Late Palaeozoic, after subduction associated with Iapetus closure had ceased, a new tectonic regime was initiated, generally dominated by extensional movement. This was associated with a phase of rifting in the Arctic–North Atlantic domain (Ziegler, 1988) which heralded the opening of the North Atlantic Ocean in the Mesozoic, and the opening of the north-east Atlantic between Greenland and Europe in the early Palaeogene. Many of the faults initiated or reactivated during the Caledonian orogeny were again reactivated as normal faults during this lengthy, but intermittent, episode of tectonism (Johnson and Frost, 1977).

South of the Highland Boundary Fault, the extensively developed Devonian rocks are of continental facies. Deposition

was discontinuous, for an unconformity between the Lower and Upper Old Red Sandstone marks uplift and erosion during Middle Devonian times (Mykura, 1983). A tensional regime led to the development of Carboniferous basins in parts of north-western Britain (Stein, 1988; Chadwick and Holliday, 1991), and marine and deltaic sediments were deposited in them. Significant Carboniferous sediments are also preserved west of the southern part of the Malin–Hebrides area in the Donegal Basin (Tate and Dobson, 1989).

Late Palaeozoic igneous activity related to crustal tension is recorded by the presence of Permo-Carboniferous dykes which occur in the report area as far north as Lewis and Harris. In the Firth of Clyde region, the eruption of Carboniferous plateau basalts is also evidence of early rifting in the Arctic–North Atlantic province (Haszeldine and Russell, 1987; Ziegler, 1988; Smythe, 1989).

Within the established structural framework, basinal development continued during the Permo-Triassic and Mesozoic. Rifting in the North Atlantic province (Smythe, 1989) was a manifestation of the tensional forces which drove continuing basin development, perhaps followed in the late Mesozoic by flexural subsidence due to stretching in the Rockall rift zone (Scrutton, 1986). During the Permo-Triassic, partly syndepositional normal movement on the major faults led to the development of several Mesozoic basins in the report area (Evans et al., 1982). These faults controlled the development of the asymmetrical half-grabens over much of the Malin–Hebrides area, and up to 5500 m of Permo-Triassic and later Mesozoic sediments have been preserved offshore.

Permo-Triassic sediments are dominantly terrestrial redbeds, indicating lower relative sea levels than those pertaining during much of the Carboniferous. Following the Rhaetian transgression, the marginal marine sediments of the Jurassic provide detailed evidence of an overall eustatic rise in sea level. Variations in this overall rise provided the principal mechanism for facies changes in the Malin–Hebrides area, and during the Late Cretaceous much of the area was probably submerged (Haq et al., 1987). Despite regional uplift, this led to a maximum sea-level stand as the rifting which was characteristic of the Mesozoic ceased in the Atlantic, and plate movement was concentrated in the opening of the Labrador Sea (Smythe, 1989). With the subsequent easing of the tensional regime, north-west Europe became tectonically quiescent.

At the close of the Cretaceous, continued regional uplift in northern Britain caused the emergence of the continental landmass. Tertiary uplift may be related to plate movement in the opening north-east Atlantic with its associated thermal activity, followed by the effects of the onset of Alpine plate collision (Ziegler, 1981). Volcanism during the Paleocene to early Eocene may have been associated with high heat-flow and the updoming of the west Scottish shelf. This episode included the emplacement of north-westerly trending dyke swarms, the development of volcanic centres in the Hebridean area, the extrusion of plateau basalts, and sill intrusion. The volcanic centres tend not to occur within the Mesozoic basins but rather along the intervening basement ridges (Hallam, 1983).

Local postvolcanic subsidence led to the development of a number of mid-Tertiary (Oligocene) sedimentary basins (Figures 3 and 4). In some cases, the subsidence was accompanied or followed by further movement on a number of bounding structures such as the Minch and Tow Valley faults. In the Canna Basin, deposition of Oligocene sediments occurred in a downwarped basinal structure that may have developed above a basement fault (Stein, 1988). With the continued opening of the north-east Atlantic, the Hebridean province became tectonically quiescent once more as the largely uplifted land area was denuded. However, late

Neogene movement of up to 150 m on the Camasunary Fault east of Rum, and on the Skerryvore Fault south-east of Coll has been proposed by Le Couer (1988) on the basis of morphological evidence. During the late Pleistocene and early Holocene, there were isostatic movements during and after glaciation, as evidenced by raised beaches on the west coast of Scotland. Only minor fault movement was associated with these readjustments (Sissons and Cornish, 1982).

THE POST-CARBONIFEROUS SEDIMENTARY BASINS

North Lewis and North Minch basins

The development of the North Lewis and North Minch basins (Figure 4) has been largely influenced by movement along the Outer Isles Thrust and Minch Fault. The Outer Isles Thrust bounds the North Lewis Basin to the west; the Minch Fault bounds both the North Lewis Basin to the east and the North Minch Basin to the west. The North Minch Basin is a half-graben on the eastern side of which Permo-Triassic sediments unconformably overlie rocks of Torridonian and Lewisian age. The Permo-Triassic rocks are in turn overlain by Jurassic and perhaps younger rocks towards the central part of the basin. The North Lewis Basin contains Permian to Jurassic sediments which rest upon the very low-angle, listric, fault surface of the Outer Isles Thrust (Figure 11). During the Late Palaeozoic, rifting in the North Atlantic led to *en-échelon,* normal reactivation of the Outer Isles Thrust (Stein, 1988), resulting in basin development on the hanging wall of that fault, with the Minch Fault developed as a steeper, possibly listric, normal fault. Stein (1988) suggests that shear movement accompanied normal movement, causing *en-échelon* faulting and the development of the Ness Shear Zone.

Late Palaeozoic fault movements led to the initiation of sediment accumulation in the basins, perhaps during the Carboniferous (Stein, 1988), although well 156/17-1 (Figure 1) proved no Upper Palaeozoic strata between the Torridonian and Permo-Triassic sediments in the North Minch Basin. Continuing rifting in the North Atlantic led to movement which allowed the deposition of 5500 m of Permo-Triassic and later Mesozoic sediments on the downthrown (eastern) side of the Minch Fault, which also shows post-Early Jurassic movement (BGS Lewis Solid Geology sheet). The sediments include the Permo-Triassic conglomerates and sandstones of the Stornoway Formation. In the North Lewis Basin, a similar but thinner sequence of sediments is preserved. Tertiary igneous activity in the North Minch Basin is concentrated in one major dyke which is marked by a striking north-north-westerly trending magnetic anomaly (Ofoegbu and Bott, 1985); some minor intrusions are present in the eastern part of the North Lewis Basin.

Sea of the Hebrides–Little Minch Trough

The Sea of the Hebrides–Little Minch Trough is separated from the North Minch Basin by the north-westerly trending Rubha Reidh Ridge (Figure 4), which has a core of Torridonian sediments (BGS Lewis Solid Geology sheet). Stein (1988) refers to this ridge as the Mid-Minch High, and suggests that it was the locus of basin inversion during latest Jurassic to mid-Cretaceous times. The ridge is likely to be of some structural significance as it forms the northern limit of widespread Tertiary igneous activity on the inner shelf. There are no volcanic centres either in the trough or on land to the north of the ridge, and the numerous dolerite dykes and sills

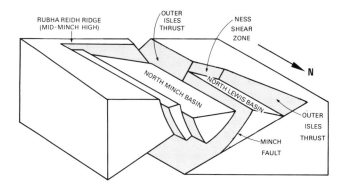

Figure 11 Isometric sketch showing the structural controls on the development of the North Lewis and North Minch basins, and the relationship between the Outer Isles Thrust and the Minch Fault. After Stein (1988).

which are characteristic of the Sea of the Hebrides–Little Minch Trough are also largely absent.

Like the North Minch Basin, the Sea of the Hebrides–Little Minch Trough owes its development to movement on the Minch Fault, which bounds the basin to the west and separates it from the extensive Lewisian rocks of the Outer Hebrides Platform. Like the North Minch Basin, the trough developed on the eastern side of the Minch Fault, which formed *en échelon* to the reactivated Outer Isles Thrust (Figure 11). It is a half-graben, overlapping Lewisian and Torridonian rocks. On its eastern margin, Carboniferous strata (Stein, 1988) in the deepest part of the basin to the west are overlain by 2500 m of Permo-Triassic to Cretaceous sediments (BGS Little Minch Solid Geology sheet). On Skye and in a large area to the south-west, the sediments are covered by early Palaeogene basalt.

The extrusion of lavas was accompanied by high heat-flow rates, regional uplift and crustal tension (Emeleus, 1983), and was followed by regional downwarping overprinted by more localized subsidence. In the Canna Basin (Figure 12), subsidence led to the deposition of over 1000 m of late Oligocene sediments over basalt (Smythe and Kenolty, 1975). To the south-east of Harris, a small outcrop of late Oligocene terrestrial sediment (Figure 3) adjacent to the Minch Fault (Evans et al., 1991) indicates that the fault was active around that time; such late movement cannot be demonstrated for the majority of faults in the report area.

Stanton Trough and Coll Basin

South of the Sea of the Hebrides–Little Minch Trough lies a ridge of Lewisian and Torridonian basement rocks which runs from the north Scottish mainland through south-eastern Skye, Coll and Tiree to the southernmost portion of the Outer Hebrides Platform, the Stanton Banks. Two small Permo-Triassic basins, the Stanton Trough and the Coll Basin, have been identified on this ridge (Figure 4).

The Stanton Trough trends largely north-north-west, counter to the general Caledonide trend of the Mesozoic basins; it is bounded to the west by the faulted edge of the Stanton Banks, and to the south by the Skerryvore Fault, which throws down to the south-east. Its eastern edge may be faulted along some of its length, but in the main, sediments onlap the Lewisian of Skerryvore Bank. To the north, the sediments are in part a continuation of those in the Sea of the Hebrides–Little Minch Trough. Up to 500 m of Permo-Triassic and perhaps Jurassic sediments may be present in the Stanton Trough (BGS Tiree Solid Geology sheet).

The Coll Basin forms an outlier bounded to the north-west by a north-easterly trending normal fault, and contains up to 500 m of probable Permo-Triassic sediments (BGS Tiree Solid Geology sheet). The trend of this basin follows the structural grain of the region.

Inner Hebrides Trough

The Inner Hebrides Trough is a complex half-graben lying to the east of the basement high which runs from the north Scottish mainland to the Stanton Banks (Figure 4). At the northern end of the basin in Skye, the Camasunary Fault bounds the basin to the west; in the south it is bounded by the Skerryvore Fault. The relationship between these two faults is uncertain; Binns et al. (1974b) originally considered them to be a single structure, but any connection is hidden by Palaeogene basalts. Although faulted against Lewisian east of Coll, the basalts have an erosive limit farther north where the line of the fault becomes ill defined on the Bouguer gravity anomaly map (Figure 5), suggesting that in this section the throw is at least much reduced. It has been speculated that the Skerryvore Fault may continue north-eastwards, crossing the Inner Hebrides Trough to join the Strathconon Fault rather than swinging northwards to the Camasunary Fault (Evans et al., 1982). The eastern margin of the trough is the inactive edge of the half-graben, where the sediments onlap Lewisian, Torridonian and Moine rocks. In the south, the basin is divided from the Malin Basin at the Blackstones Bank igneous centre, and is bounded to the south-east by the Dubh Artach Fault, a part of the Great Glen fault complex.

Along the axis of the Inner Hebrides Trough, there appears to be a thinning of the Mesozoic sequence, which may represent a buried basement ridge (BGS Tiree Solid Geology sheet). This trough is overlain in its central part by a thick sequence of Tertiary basalts, and in the south by Tertiary sediments of the Blackstones Basin. Gravity modelling (BGS Tiree Solid Geology sheet) suggests that the base of the lavas is more or less horizontal, indicating that unlike the Sea of the Hebrides–Little Minch Trough, there was no downwarping after basalt intrusion. Nevertheless, Tertiary movement on at least part of the Skerryvore Fault is demonstrated by basalts being faulted against the Lewisian east of Coll, and

from the juxtaposition of the Lewisian and the Tertiary (?late Oligocene) sediments (Figure 3).

Colonsay and Malin basins

South of the Inner Hebrides Trough, the Dubh Artach and Colonsay faults are recognised as splays in the Great Glen Fault complex, and formed a locus for the development of the Colonsay and Malin basins (Figure 4). Evidence for the timing of fault movement on the Colonsay and Dubh Artach faults is sparse, but like the rest of the Great Glen fault zone, they may have been reactivated by Variscan movement during the Carboniferous (Kennedy, 1979). The Dubh Artach Fault appears to have been active from Late Carboniferous through to Mesozoic times, resulting in a thick sequence of sediments in the Colonsay Basin, which lies to the south-east of the fault. Movement probably continued during the Permian and Mesozoic, with the deposition of over 4000 m of Late- and post-Palaeozoic sediments (BGS Tiree Solid Geology sheet). In the north-eastern part of the Colonsay Basin, Jurassic rocks occur at outcrop, whereas in the south-west, Mesozoic strata are overlain by Oligocene sediments that are likely to be an extension of those of the Blackstones Basin. To the north-east, the basin is pinched out between the Dubh Artach and Colonsay faults to the south of Mull.

To the south-east of the Colonsay Fault, which forms the south-eastern boundary of the Colonsay Basin, metasediments of both the Dalradian and the Colonsay Group form a basement ridge which runs from the island of Colonsay south-westwards to Ireland; this is termed the Islay–Donegal Platform (Figure 4).

Like the Colonsay Basin, the Malin Basin is bounded to the south-east by the Islay–Donegal Platform, although in the south, Permian to Mesozoic sediments extend south-eastwards beyond the line of the Colonsay Fault and unconformably overlie Moine/Dalradian metasediments. To the north, the Malin Basin is bounded by the southernmost identified portion of the Skerryvore Fault, and the west-north-westerly trending Stanton Fault. The youngest known rocks in the Malin Basin are of Early Jurassic age (Evans et al., 1982). To the west, the Malin Basin extends towards the Donegal Basin, where sands, silts and clays of Westphalian

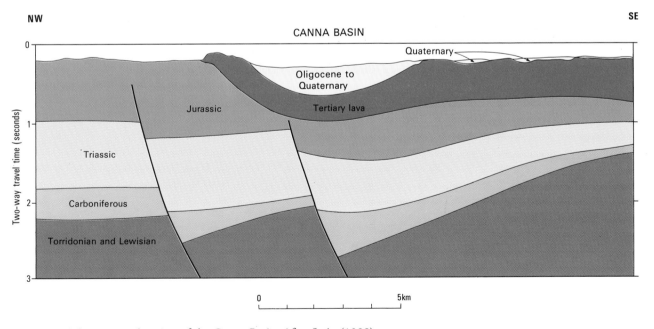

Figure 12 The structural setting of the Canna Basin. After Stein (1988).

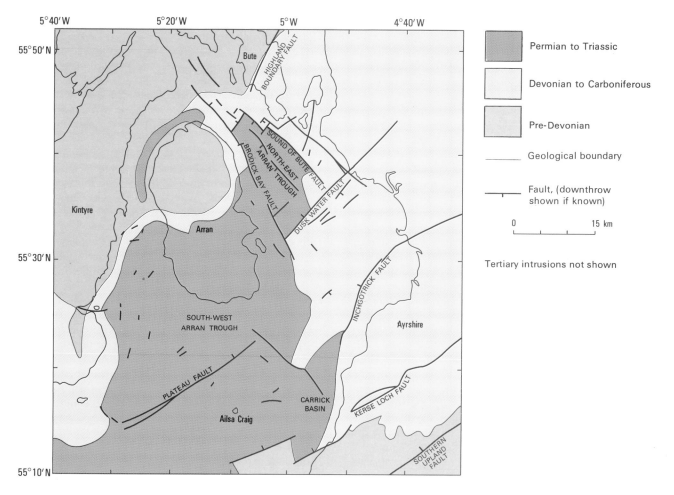

Figure 13 The fault pattern in the Firth of Clyde region. The Caledonian north-easterly trend is accompanied by more local north-westerly trending structures. After Deegan (1978).

age have been drilled beneath a Permian and younger sequence (Tate and Dobson, 1989). Thus the possibility of Carboniferous sediments underlying the Malin Basin or other troughs in the region cannot be ruled out. Indeed, with postulated Variscan movement on the Great Glen fault zone and associated faults, Carboniferous strata may also be present in the Colonsay Basin.

Loch Indaal Basin and Rathlin Trough

South-east of the Islay–Donegal Platform, the Leannan–Loch Gruinart Fault forms the north-western margin of the Loch Indaal Basin (Dobson et al., 1975). A geographical continuity can be demonstrated between the Leannan Fault, the Loch Gruinart Fault and the Great Glen Fault, although continuity of structural character and history has been doubted by Westbrook and Borradaile (1978), and an important branch of the fault may cut across western Islay (Figure 4). The Loch Indaal Basin takes the form of an asymmetric half-graben with an infill of Permo-Triassic and Jurassic sediments (see Figure 30); the older sediments onlap the Dalradian metasediments of the Middle Bank to the south-east. To the south-west, the basin is bounded by a north-westerly trending fault, one of a number of counter-Caledonide structures in the area (BGS Malin Solid Geology sheet). In the northern part of the basin, shallow-seismic evidence indicates the presence of intrabasinal, north-easterly trending faulting and folding along the axis of the basin (Evans et al., 1979). Borehole evidence suggests that the Leannan–Loch Gruinart Fault has been active since the deposition of Lias sediment.

To the south-east of the Middle Bank lies the Rathlin Trough (Figure 4). This basin is controlled to the north-west and south-east by the Foyle and Tow Valley faults respectively. The Foyle Fault may extend north-eastwards to join the Ericht–Laidon Fault, and the Tow Valley Fault may have connections to the Tyndrum Fault (Pitcher, 1969; Evans et al., 1979). The Tow Valley Fault separates the Rathlin Trough from the largely Dalradian Highland Border Ridge, whose rocks can be closely correlated with those of Kintyre. The Rathlin Trough contains strata of Carboniferous to Tertiary age (Evans et al., 1979), and sediments of probable Triassic age extend north-westwards to overlap the line of the Foyle Fault and unconformably overlie the Dalradian metasediments of the Middle Bank. The Tow Valley Fault is an important bounding structure that probably experienced normal movement in Carboniferous times. On its downthrown north-western side onshore, lying upon basalt, are small basins containing late Oligocene clays (Griffith et al., 1987; see Figure 37). Both the basalt and sediments are displaced by the fault, demonstrating movement at least into late Oligocene times.

North Channel Basin and the Firth of Clyde region

In the Firth of Clyde and the North Channel, fault trends are commonly perpendicular to the Caledonide trend (Figures 4 and 13). McLean (1978) attributed this to localised strain during Ordovician to Devonian times, resulting in local crustal thinning. On the other hand, seismic-refraction studies (Bamford, 1979) suggest that the crust beneath the Midland Valley is thicker than beneath the Caledonian foreland to the north. The differences in structural pattern between the Firth of Clyde region and other parts of the Malin–Hebrides area may therefore be related more to the influences of Old Red Sandstone basin development, which was constrained by the Highland Boundary and Southern Upland faults.

South-east of the Tow Valley Fault, the North Channel Basin has a north-westerly axis and may contain over 1000 m of Permo-Triassic sediments directly overlying the Devonian (BGS Clyde Solid Geology sheet). From the Tow Valley Fault, the basin runs south-eastwards between the older rocks of Northern Ireland and Scotland. The basin has no well-defined faulted margins, but McLean and Deegan (1978) have identified north-westerly trending faults within the basin. To the east, the Stranraer Basin has a similar structural trend and contains up to 1200 m of Permo-Triassic sandstone (Lovell, 1983). Comparably aligned basins are also found farther to the east in the Southern Uplands. The North Channel Basin cuts across the lines of both the Highland Boundary and Southern Upland faults, although neither fault appears to have affected its development, and neither is evident on seismic-reflection sections through the North Channel (BGS Clyde Solid Geology sheet; Hall et al., 1984).

To the north-east, in the Firth of Clyde, the Permo-Triassic rocks of the South-West Arran Trough and the North-East Arran Trough are bounded to the north-west by Devonian and Carboniferous sediments lying on the south-eastern flank of the Highland Border Ridge. The dominant trend here appears to be Caledonian, with the Plateau Fault, Dusk Water Fault and the offshore extrapolation of the Inchgotrick Fault (McLean and Deegan, 1978) forming significant bounding features (Figure 13). The Highland Boundary Fault, which forms a major structural lineament to the north-east, becomes less well defined to the south-west of the Island of Bute. It is believed to occur within the Dalradian outcrop on the Island of Arran (British Geological Survey, 1987), and to have been affected by the emplacement of the Northern Granite, but it has not been traced farther south-west and does not apparently control the north-western margin of the South-West Arran Trough. Nevertheless, some authors consider that this major dislocation continues across Ireland (e.g. Hutton, 1987; Coward, 1990).

The Plateau Fault can be identified forming the south-eastern boundary of the south-easterly facing South-West Arran Trough half-graben (McLean and Deegan, 1978). Gravity data indicate that the zone of dislocation continues to the north-east, and may run into the Dusk Water Fault (Figure 13). Deep-seismic profiling shows that the Plateau Fault has a north-westerly downthrow of up to 2500 m at the top of the Lower Old Red Sandstone, although Permo-Triassic sediments are downthrown by only 300 m, and extend south-eastwards over the area around Ailsa Craig. East of Ailsa Craig lies the Permo-Triassic Carrick Basin, whose eastern boundary is formed by a north–south-trending extension of the Inchgotrick Fault.

The North-East Arran Trough is cut by the north-westerly trending Brodick Bay and Sound of Bute faults (Figure 13), the latter forming the north-eastern boundary of the Permo-Triassic outcrop. There is little conclusive evidence on the relationship between the Dusk Water–Plateau Fault and the Brodick Bay Fault, but McLean and Deegan (1978) favour the former being formed en échelon to, rather than displaced by, the Brodick Bay Fault. Nevertheless, the Brodick Bay and the Sound of Bute faults demonstrate that the north-west to south-east structural trend is important in the Firth of Clyde region.

3 Precambrian and Lower Palaeozoic

A wide variety of Precambrian to Early Palaeozoic rocks are present in the Malin–Hebrides area, the oldest of which date back to over 2900 Ma. The main divisions are the Lewisian, Torridonian and Moine assemblages, all of Precambrian age, and the largely upper Proterozoic Dalradian Supergroup. Cambrian, Ordovician and Silurian strata are also present. These basement rocks form much the greater part of the landscape surrounding the report area, but are less common in submarine outcrop. Nevertheless, they make up approximately a third of the offshore area. Several boreholes have penetrated the basement offshore, where it has been mapped chiefly from geophysical information, although much of the interpretation has come from extrapolation of onshore sections.

The distribution of the basement outcrop is to a large extent controlled by the major dislocations that cross the area: the Outer Isles Thrust, the Moine Thrust, the Great Glen–Loch Gruinart–Leannan fault system, the Highland Boundary Fault and the Southern Upland Fault (Figure 14). These are important structures of some antiquity (see Chapter 2), and have in many cases been subjected to repeated phases of reactivation during their long histories. The Outer Isles Thrust, for example, is believed first to have been active around 1700 Ma, and then from 1200 to 1100 Ma when movement was possibly in a normal sense (Lailey et al., 1989). Further movement is inferred to have taken place during the Caledonian orogeny when the Moine Thrust to the east marked the main orogenic front. The main outcrop of pre-Caledonide rocks, formed of Lewisian, Torridonian and Cambrian strata, therefore lies to the west of the Moine Thrust. Relatively weakly metamorphosed Torridonian and Cambro-Ordovician rocks are known to occur only between the Moine Thrust and the Outer Isles Thrust. On the shelf to the west of the Outer Isles Thrust, the only basement rocks so far found are Lewisian.

The metamorphic Caledonides to the east of the Moine Thrust form part of a large tract of metamorphic rocks which can be traced in eastern Greenland and western Norway (Figure 15). These comprise the Moine and Dalradian assemblages that have been subjected to Caledonian deformation, although both appear to have been affected by earlier Proterozoic deformational events (see Chapter 2). On mainland Scotland, the Moine is confined to an area bounded to the south-east by the Great Glen Fault, and to the west by the Moine Thrust; the Dalradian outcrop is restricted to the region between the Highland Boundary and Great Glen faults (Figure 14).

The main outcrop of Ordovician and Silurian strata lies to the south-east of the Southern Upland Fault, although inliers are present in the dominantly Upper Palaeozoic rocks of the Midland Valley, and there is a wedge-shaped outcrop of Ordovician rocks around Ballantrae (Figure 14). These rocks represent deposition on the margins of an 'American' Laurentian continent. This lay to the north of the Iapetus Ocean which separated it from the 'European' continent of Avalonia, and which now forms the southern part of the British Isles. The Iapetus Ocean closed during the Caledonian orogeny, and the suture or convergence zone between these two ancient continents now forms a north-westerly dipping zone beneath the Southern Uplands (Chadwick and Holliday, 1991) (Figure 15). The plate-tectonic move-

ment also provided the driving mechanism for some of the deformation in the Moine and Dalradian rocks of Scotland and Ireland, and resulted in the intrusion of large granites.

Marine survey techniques rarely allow the subdivision of metamorphic assemblages offshore. Some rock types may be broadly differentiated on a large scale by gravity and magnetic methods, but due to lack of penetration of heavily indurated rock, shallow-seismic profiles provide little real evidence. On such records, basement can be identified by a lack of internal structure together with a strongly reflecting upper surface that may be characterised by hyperbolic reflectors. Such characteristics are common to all hard basement rocks, but the topographic style of the bedrock can sometimes provide a basis for differentiation. This is particularly the case nearshore, where the onshore geology and topography can to some extent be extrapolated offshore. Figure 16 shows a sparker section from the eastern part of The Minch where Lewisian rocks are likely to form the sea bed in the east, but Torridonian sediments may create the higher peaks farther offshore.

LEWISIAN

The Lewisian Complex (Watson, 1975) is the collective name given to the oldest rocks in the UK; these form the Archaean/early Proterozoic basement craton of north-western Scotland. The complex comprises a series of quartzofeldspathic gneisses together with a wide variety of basic and ultrabasic components. These represent dominantly metamorphosed, acid to ultrabasic igneous rocks with subordinate metamorphosed sediments. Rocks of the complex can be dated back to at least 2900 Ma, but they have been repeatedly modified by subsequent tectonic and metamorphic reworking (Figure 17).

Two main phases of tectonic and metamorphic activity gave rise to the Scourian Complex, and the later Laxfordian Complex (Watson, 1983). The earliest recorded activity in the Archaean led to the formation of the early Scourian, or Badcallian, gneiss complex. The rocks were locally, but extensively, reworked during the Inverian episode at around 2400 Ma, and later during the Laxfordian at around 1800 Ma (Fettes and Mendum, 1987). In particular, late Laxfordian activity was marked by the intrusion of granite sheets and pegmatites at around 1700 Ma, and was ended with intrusion of minor microdiorite at around 1400 Ma.

Onshore, the Lewisian is chiefly found to the west of the Moine Thrust on the north-west Scottish mainland, and in the Outer Hebrides, although in the Northern Highlands, particularly around the Sound of Sleat, several thrust slices of Lewisian have been mapped within the Moine. The major outcrops have been extrapolated offshore (Figure 14). In the Caledonian foreland of north-west Scotland, the Lewisian is overlain in places by erosional remnants of Torridonian sandstones; the outcrops of these two groups, which do not appear to follow a regional pattern, can be followed offshore for up to 15 km into The Minch, where they are overlain by Permo-Triassic sediments. Most submarine outcrop in this area can be identified only as undivided basement, for any differentiation between Lewisian and Torridonian rocks on seismic records is very tentative (Figure 16).

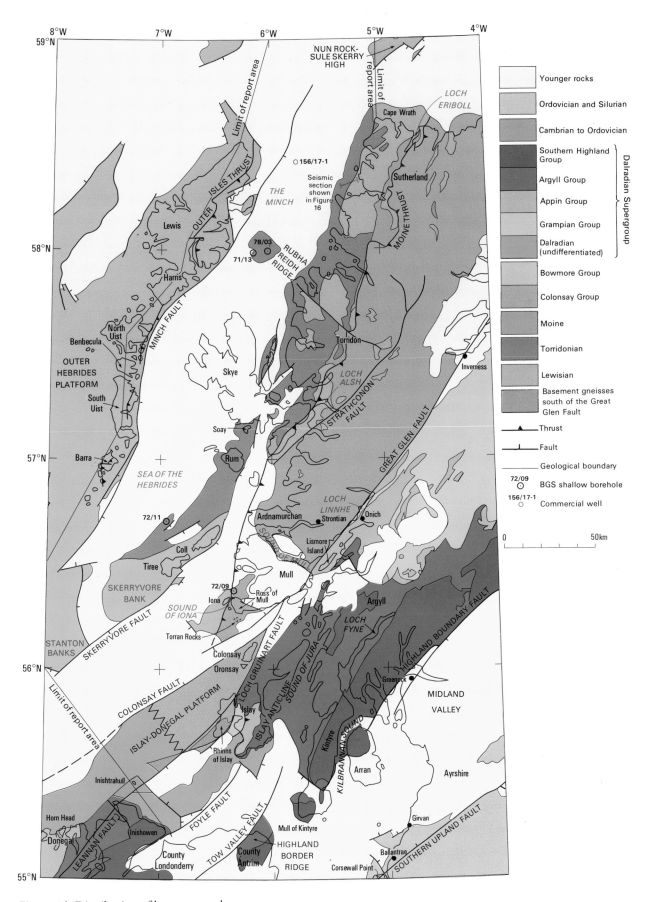

Figure 14 Distribution of basement rocks.

19

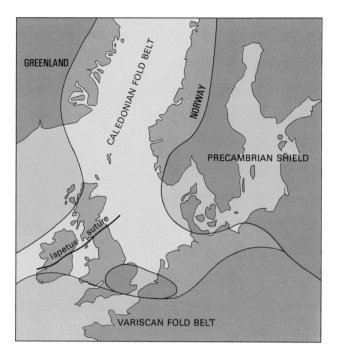

Figure 15 Pre-spreading relationship of Caledonian and later orogenic belts in the Arctic–North Atlantic region. After Ziegler (1981) and Higgins and Phillips (1979).

To the north-east of The Minch lies the Nun Rock–Sule Skerry High (Figure 14), an intrabasinal basement high within the West Orkney Basin. A sample from the south-western end of the submarine outcrop proved to be pink, biotite gneiss of Lewisian type (BGS Sutherland Solid Geology sheet). The most extensive onshore exposure of the Lewisian rocks in Scotland occurs in the Outer Hebrides. In Lewis and northern Harris, the dominant lithology is grey, granodioritic, quartzofeldspathic gneiss. The generally low relief in the north rises southwards to the more rugged terrain formed by the anorthosites and metagabbros of the South Harris Igneous Complex. Farther south, the gneisses of North and South Uist, Benbecula and Barra produce a

varied terrain with characteristically high cliffs in the east falling away to sandy machair in the west. The Lewisian rocks of the Outer Hebrides can be traced offshore to the west (Figure 14), where they form an extensive outcrop known as the Outer Hebrides Platform (BGS St Kilda Solid Geology sheet; Stoker et al., in press). Over this platform, gravity anomaly contours form a north-north-easterly trending pattern in which the anomalies generally increase in amplitude eastwards (McQuillin and Watson, 1973). To the east of the Outer Hebrides, the submarine outcrop can be traced only a short distance to the Minch Fault, where it is downthrown and overlain by a thick sequence of sedimentary rocks.

To the south of the Outer Hebrides lie the Stanton Banks, the southernmost portion of the Outer Hebrides Platform (Figure 14). Interpretation of gravity data provides evidence here of regional variation in rock type; an elongate north-east-trending positive Bouguer anomaly in the south-eastern corner of the banks contrasts with lower gravity anomalies to the north (Figure 18). This variation is interpreted as being due to more basic, possibly granulitic gneisses in the south, but more acidic, possibly quartzofeldspathic gneisses in the north (Evans et al., 1980). Samples collected from the Stanton Banks by divers comprise granites and dark, foliated gneisses. Two samples of microcline-granite with perthitic microcline, albite-oligoclase, quartz and biotite were reported by Binns et al. (1974b) to be similar to known late Laxfordian granites. A Rb-Sr date obtained from one of the granite samples gave a late Laxfordian age of between 1600 and 1400 Ma (BGS Tiree Solid Geology sheet).

In the Sea of the Hebrides, the Lewisian of the Skerryvore Bank extends north-eastwards to embrace the islands of Coll and Tiree (Figure 14). Outcrops on these islands comprise acid, quartzofeldspathic gneisses with abundant zones of metasediments of arkosic, arenaceous, calcareous and dolomitic affinity (Phemister, 1960). Offshore samples from this block include gneiss and scapolite-bearing marble (BGS Tiree Solid Geology sheet). This diversity of lithologies results in considerable variety in gravity anomaly values over the bank. The Bouguer gravity anomaly map (Figure 5) displays a low to the west-south-west of Tiree that has been

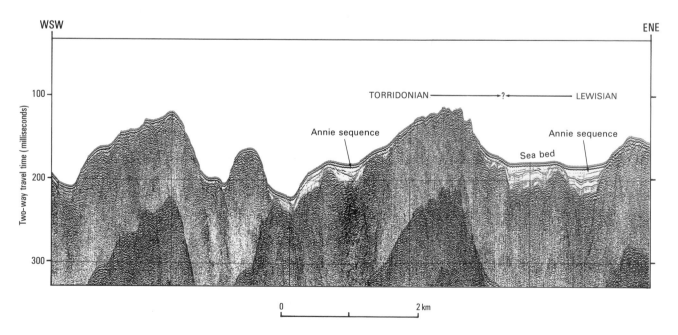

Figure 16 Shallow-seismic (sparker) profile showing Precambrian rocks and Quaternary sediments off the west coast of Sutherland. For location see Figure 14.

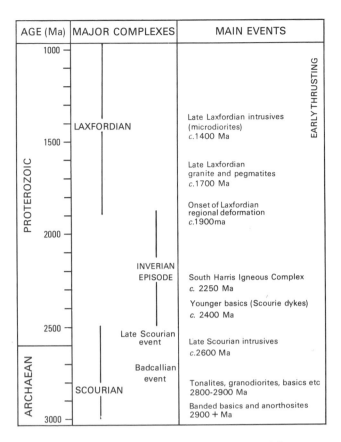

AGE (Ma)	MAJOR COMPLEXES	MAIN EVENTS	
1000			EARLY THRUSTING
1500	LAXFORDIAN	Late Laxfordian intrusives (microdiorites) *c.*1400 Ma	
		Late Laxfordian granite and pegmatites *c.*1700 Ma	
2000		Onset of Laxfordian regional deformation *c.*1900ma	
	INVERIAN EPISODE	South Harris Igneous Complex *c.* 2250 Ma	
2500		Younger basics (Scourie dykes) *c.* 2400 Ma	
	Late Scourian event	Late Scourian intrusives *c.*2600 Ma	
	Badcallian event		
	SCOURIAN	Tonalites, granodiorites, basics etc 2800-2900 Ma	
3000		Banded basics and anorthosites 2900 + Ma	

(PROTEROZOIC / ARCHAEAN labels on left side)

Figure 17 The main events in the development of the Lewisian Complex. After Fettes and Mendum (1987).

modelled as representing a stock-like granitic body some 15 km in diameter that comes close to the surface (BGS Tiree Solid Geology sheet).

Lewisian marble and pelitic metasediments are also found in the dominantly pink, acid gneiss of the island of Iona (Figure 14), which lies at the northern end of a basement inlier from which samples of acidic and biotite-hornblende gneiss have been collected by divers (Barber et al., 1979). This inlier lies immediately to the west of the Moine outcrops of the Ross of Mull; the Moine Thrust has been interpreted as lying within the Sound of Iona.

BASEMENT GNEISSES SOUTH OF THE GREAT GLEN FAULT

The most southerly occurrences of gneisses in the report area are the relatively small blocks that occur in the Islay–Inishowen region, near the Leannan–Loch Gruinart fault system. Onshore parts of these blocks form the Rhinns of Islay and the island of Inishtrahull (Figure 14). The Rhinns of Islay comprise strongly foliated, metamorphosed rocks of an acidic to ultrabasic composition, intruded by syenitic sheets (Marcantonio et al., 1988). The gneisses of Inishtrahull are correlatable with those of the Rhinns of Islay, and were taken as being Lewisian, both from their structural history (Bowes and Hopgood, 1975) and from isotopic analysis (Macintyre et al, 1975; Daly et al., 1991). However, Marcantonio et al. (1988) and Fitches et al. (1990) do not consider them to be part of the Lewisian Complex, but rather an allochthonous terrane emplaced at around 1800 Ma. Furthermore, Dickin and Bowes (1991) obtained a Sm-Nd model age of 1960 ±20 Ma for the original formation of the gneiss complex of Inishtrahull, significantly younger than the Lewisian. Radiometric dating of

offshore samples collected on the Inishtrahull Platform gave an age of 1710 Ma, and mineral assemblages suggest amphibolite facies metamorphism (BGS Malin Solid Geology sheet). The isolated block of basement mapped between the Rhinns of Islay and Inishtrahull has been assigned to the same terrane on seismic evidence (Evans, 1974).

TORRIDONIAN

Outcrops of upper Proterozoic Torridonian rocks on the north-western Scottish mainland and the Inner Hebrides comprise largely unmetamorphosed sediments, predominantly arkosic sandstones, siltstones and mudstones. Torridonian strata are restricted to the zone between the Outer Isles Thrust and the Moine Thrust (Figure 14), where they lie with marked unconformity on Lewisian basement, and characteristically form mountains including many isolated peaks

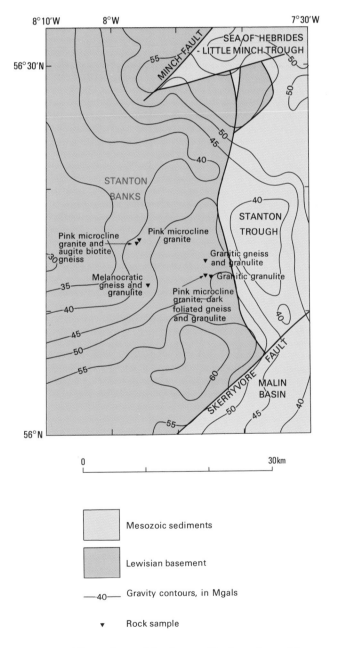

Figure 18 The geology of the Stanton Banks region, with superimposed Bouguer gravity anomalies. See Figure 5 for location of the area covered by the diagram.

21

AGE	LITHOSTRATIGRAPHY		LITHOLOGICAL DIVISIONS
LATE PROTEROZOIC, PRECAMBRIAN	TORRIDON GROUP	AULTBEA FORMATION	Argillaceous sediments
		APPLECROSS FORMATION	Fine to coarse-grained red sandstones
		DIABAIG FORMATION	Basal fanglomerate
	STOER GROUP		Fanglomerate and fluvial sediments
	SLEAT GROUP		Deltaic facies

Figure 19 Torridonian stratigraphy.

in Sutherland as well as the Torridon Mountains themselves (see Front Cover). The Torridonian reaches an aggregate total thickness of around 7000 m, and is subdivided (Figure 19) into the Sleat, Stoer and Torridon groups (Johnson, 1983).

In Skye, the basal stratigraphical unit is the 3500 m-thick Sleat Group, consisting of coarse-grained, grey, fluvial sandstones and subordinate lacustrine or shallow-marine shales that have been subjected to very low-grade metamorphism (Nicholson, 1991). Palaeocurrent directions suggest a similar pattern of sedimentation to the Stoer Group, with the sea lying to the east (Sutton and Watson, 1964), but the Sleat Group facies is predominantly deltaic.

The 2000 m-thick Stoer Group occurs as the basal unit to the north of Skye, where it comprises redbeds deposited in alluvial-fan, fluvial, aeolian and ephemeral-lacustrine environments in a semiarid climate (Stewart, 1988). The sediments are interpreted as having been deposited in a small basin, possibly a rift-graben (Stewart, 1988), but perhaps bounded to the west by the Proterozoic Outer Isles Thrust (Lailey et al., 1989). The sediments show easterly palaeocurrent directions (Williams, 1969), and palaeomagnetic evidence suggests that deposition occurred at around latitude 10° to 15°N (Torsvik and Sturt, 1987).

The more widespread Torridon Group rests with apparent conformity on the Sleat Group, but lies with angular unconformity upon the Stoer Group (Stewart, 1969). It comprises the thickest sequence of Torridonian sediments, up to 6000 m, and consists of a local basal conglomerate overlain by red arkosic sandstones and argillaceous sediments. The group is subdivided into the Diabaig, Applecross and Aultbea formations (Figure 19). Lacustrine sediments and locally developed fanglomerates of the Diabaig Formation are overlain by fluvial sandstones of the Applecross and Aultbea formations, which were deposited in a warm, humid climate (Williams, 1968; 1969) at a latitude of about 35°S (Torsvik and Sturt, 1987). Nicholson (1991) considers that the Applecross Formation represents alluvial-braidplain sedimentation (Figure 20), and although this contrasts with Williams' (1969) alluvial-fan interpretation for the Applecross and Aultbea formations (Figure 21), a broadly westerly or north-westerly source is common to both models. Nicholson (1991) points out that his revised

model implies the absence of a fault bounding the basin to the west, and suggests that the Outer Isles Thrust was inactive at that time. This agrees with a structural interpretation by Lailey et al. (1989).

On shallow-seismic records, the Torridonian is generally seen as a massive sequence with no discernable traces of bedding reflectors, but rockhead topography and the character of reflectivity may be used to differentiate this group locally, as off the west coast of Sutherland (Figure 16). Also, to the north of Coll, the undulating character of the sea bed is reminiscent of a hilly Torridonian landscape. Within the report area, there are two main occurrences of Torridonian at sea-bed outcrop: in The Minch, and extending south-west from Skye (Figure 14).

In The Minch, the Rubha Reidh Ridge (Figure 14) is flanked by Mesozoic sediments both to the north and south. BGS boreholes 71/13 and 78/03, drilled on this bank, recovered fine- to coarse-grained, hard, arkosic sandstones (Evans et al., 1982). These are mineralogically similar to local Permo-Triassic sandstones, but are highly indurated, and compare with sediments of the Torridon Group, an interpretation consistent both with the structural setting and the depositional models of Nicholson (1991) and Williams (1969). Off Sutherland (Figure 14), the Lewisian and Torridonian can be traced to a maximum of some 15 km offshore before being overlapped by Permo-Triassic sediments of the North Minch Basin. Seismic interpretations indicating that Torridonian rocks underlie the Mesozoic of the North Minch Basin (BGS Sutherland Solid Geology sheet; Stein, 1988)

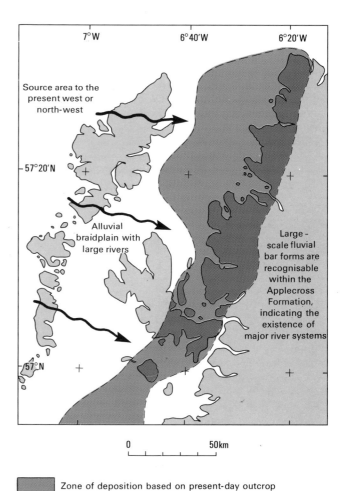

Figure 20 Depositional environment of the Applecross Formation. After Nicholson (1991).

22

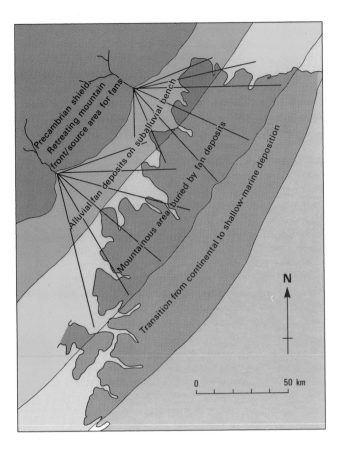

Figure 21 Depositional environment of the Applecross and Aultbea formations. After Williams (1969).

have been confirmed by well 156/17-1, which drilled 131 m of Torridonian beneath Permo-Triassic strata (see Figure 29). The sequence consists of hard, subarkosic, green, purple and grey-brown, siliceously cemented sandstone with subordinate hard, purple to grey siltstone and very hard, blocky, orange or reddish brown mudstone.

To the south, in the Sea of the Hebrides, a major Torridonian outcrop makes up part of a basement ridge extending south-westwards from Skye (Figure 14). North of Coll, the rockhead is seen to have relatively high relief that contrasts with the flatter sea bed of the Tertiary basalts to the east (see Figure 40). The south-western limit of the Torridonian is more difficult to define, as the outcrop becomes rather featureless and is not easily distinguished from the seismically poorly bedded Permo-Triassic strata that overlie it. The boundary with the Lewisian to the south-east is also indistinct. The ridge includes the Torridonian rocks of the islands of Soay and Rum, and has been sampled both with a sea-bed rockdrill and at BGS borehole 72/11. The latter recovered medium-grained, coarse-banded, red arkose (Binns et al., 1974b). The stratigraphical and geographical relationships, as well as lithological similarity with the outcrops on Soay and Rum suggest that much of this ridge is made up of Torridon Group rocks; similar rocks may extend westwards beneath the Mesozoic of the Sea of the Hebrides–Little Minch Trough (Stein, 1988).

On Colonsay, Oronsay and north-western Islay (Figure 14), rocks originally identified as Torridonian (Wilkinson, 1907) form a lithostratigraphical unit known as the Colonsay Group. They have more recently been allocated to the Dalradian (Stewart and Hackman, 1973), although this interpretation has been questioned by Fitches and Maltman

(1984). Their age is considered to be enigmatic, but they are probably not Torridonian.

MOINE

The Moine, a sequence predominantly composed of metasediments, crops out in an area of the northern Highlands bounded by the Moine Thrust and the Great Glen Fault. Three tectonostratigraphical units have been defined, namely the Morar, Glenfinnan and Loch Eil divisions, all of which are characterised by psammitic and semipelitic lithologies (Johnstone et al., 1969). Radiometric dating (Brook et al., 1977) provides a possible maximum age for these metasediments. The Morar Division postdates the Laxfordian maximum age of 1500 Ma, but is older than 1240 ±96 Ma. The Glenfinnan Division is dated as at least 1050 ±46 Ma, but the age of the Loch Eil Division, the youngest division, is not certain. The metamorphic grade of the Moine ranges from middle- to upper-amphibolite facies in the east, to greenschist facies in the west (Fettes, 1979).

The Moine rocks of the northern part of the Scottish mainland may be traced up to 15 km offshore, where they are overlain by Permo-Triassic sediments. No boreholes have been drilled in this area, so the rocks have been assigned to the Morar Division by extrapolation from onshore. In the long coastal section from Loch Alsh to Mull, the Moine outcrop can again be traced up to some 15 km from land, where it is either faulted against other basement rocks or covered by Mesozoic sediments or Tertiary extrusive rocks. The metasediments of this region are also regarded as Morar Division by extrapolation from onshore. At the northern end of the Sound of Mull, samples obtained by divers are predominantly of garnet-mica schists. The Moine also probably forms the sea floor in the Sound of Mull (BGS Argyll Solid Geology sheet).

South and west of Mull there are further outcrops of Moine. The limited onshore exposure on the Ross of Mull includes pelites and psammites which are probably equivalent to Morar and Glenfinnan division lithologies. North of the Ross of Mull, samples of psammite have been collected at the sea bed (Barber et al., 1979), and were identified in BGS borehole 72/09 (Figure 14). To the south of the Ross of Mull, samples recovered by divers have included psammite, metabasite and schist; these have been designated as undifferentiated Moine (BGS Tiree Solid Geology sheet).

In the south-west of the area, a small basement block interpreted as Moine is found near Inishtrahull. It is separated from the basement gneisses of the Inishtrahull Platform by the Leannan–Loch Gruinart fault system, and samples collected from it gave radiometric dates consistent with a Moine age (BGS Malin Solid Geology sheet). This being so, it is probable that the Moine Thrust lies to the west.

DALRADIAN

The Dalradian Supergroup (Harris et al., 1978; Harris and Pitcher, 1975) comprises mainly late Precambrian metamorphosed marine sediments laid down along the margins of the Laurentian Craton. The sedimentary pile was metamorphosed and deformed largely within the Caledonian orogeny (see Chapter 2). The outcrop of the Dalradian in the Malin–Hebrides area is confined to the area lying between the Great Glen and Highland Boundary faults. In addition to the well-documented mainland sections, the Dalradian is also present

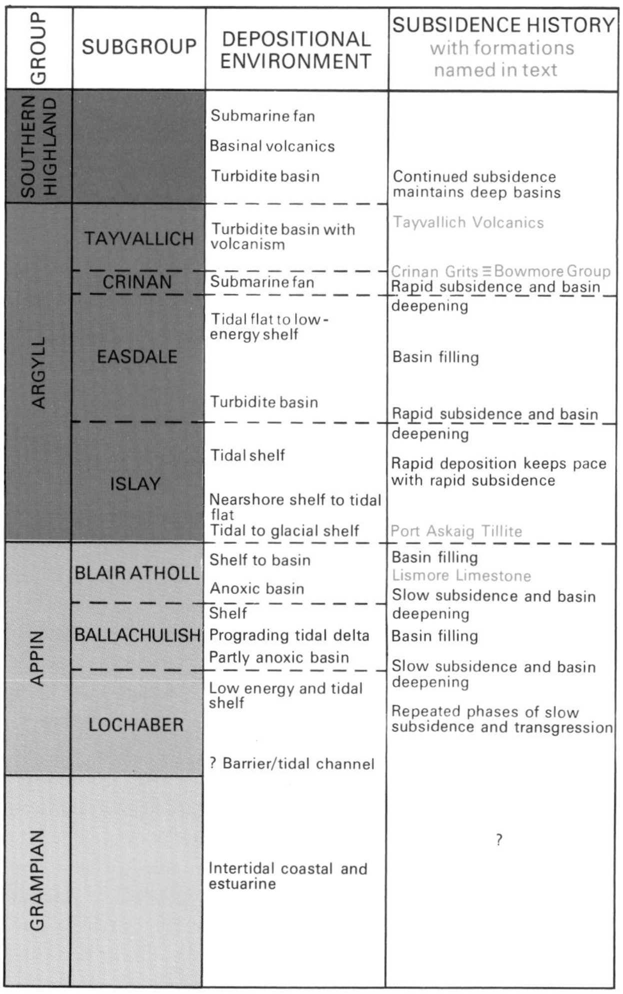

GROUP	SUBGROUP	DEPOSITIONAL ENVIRONMENT	SUBSIDENCE HISTORY with formations named in text
SOUTHERN HIGHLAND		Submarine fan	
		Basinal volcanics	
		Turbidite basin	Continued subsidence maintains deep basins
ARGYLL	TAYVALLICH	Turbidite basin with volcanism	Tayvallich Volcanics
	CRINAN	Submarine fan	Crinan Grits ≡ Bowmore Group / Rapid subsidence and basin deepening
	EASDALE	Tidal flat to low-energy shelf	Basin filling
		Turbidite basin	Rapid subsidence and basin deepening
	ISLAY	Tidal shelf	Rapid deposition keeps pace with rapid subsidence
		Nearshore shelf to tidal flat	
		Tidal to glacial shelf	Port Askaig Tillite
APPIN	BLAIR ATHOLL	Shelf to basin	Basin filling
		Anoxic basin	Lismore Limestone / Slow subsidence and basin deepening
	BALLACHULISH	Shelf	Basin filling
		Prograding tidal delta	
		Partly anoxic basin	Slow subsidence and basin deepening
	LOCHABER	Low energy and tidal shelf	Repeated phases of slow subsidence and transgression
		? Barrier/tidal channel	
GRAMPIAN		Intertidal coastal and estuarine	?

Figure 22 Lithostratigraphy, sedimentation and basin history of the Dalradian Supergroup. After Anderton (1985).

in the southern islands of the Inner Hebrides, such as Islay and Jura, and forms the largest area of submarine outcrop of Caledonide rocks in the report area (Figure 14). The grade of metamorphism seen in those metasediments close to the report area ranges from greenschist to lower-amphibolite facies (Fettes, 1979). The supergroup can be subdivided into the Grampian, Appin, Argyll and Southern Highland groups (Figure 22). The Colonsay and Bowmore groups are also discussed in this section, although they may not belong to the Dalradian Supergroup.

Grampian Group

The Grampian Group is present in the Grampian Highlands to the east and north-east of Loch Linnhe, and comprises a succession of psammites, quartzites and pelites. The only representative of this group in the report area is a 14 km-long coastal section in Loch Linnhe where flaggy psammites crop out on the eastern shore north of Onich (Figure 14). The offshore extension of these rocks is limited by the Great Glen fault zone, which is interpreted as running less than a kilometre from this coast (BGS Argyll Solid Geology sheet).

Appin Group

The Appin Group is known to be present in north-west Donegal, on Islay, and on the shores of Loch Linnhe adjacent to the Great Glen Fault (Figure 14). It is a mixed sequence of quartzites, slates and limestones deposited as shallow-water sediments (Anderton, 1985). The detailed stratigraphy developed in Donegal and Islay cannot be traced offshore, and the submarine basement outcrop is mapped as undivided Dalradian (BGS Malin Solid Geology sheet). It is nevertheless tempting to suppose that the main structure in the Appin Group of Donegal, the Horn Head Anticline (Hutton, 1979), may be correlated with the Islay Anticline (Roberts and Treagus, 1977), and that the outcrop of rocks of this age may be continuous, albeit faulted, across the Malin Sea (Evans et al., 1980; Hall et al., 1984). In northern Islay, the Appin Group in the core of the Islay Anticline plunges northeastwards beneath the Argyll Group.

Rocks on the south-eastern shore of Loch Linnhe and on Lismore Island, including the Lismore Limestone (Figure 22) of the Blair Atholl Subgroup, belong to the upper part of the Appin Group. The surrounding offshore outcrop of Dalradian is taken to be a continuation of such rocks (BGS Argyll Solid Geology sheet).

Argyll Group

The Argyll Group displays considerable lithological variation (Anderton, 1979); its base is marked by the glacially deposited Port Askaig Tillite (Figure 22), which records a widespread Precambrian glaciation (Spencer, 1971; Johnson, 1983). This is overlain by a succession of shallow-marine dolomites, quartzites, grits, graphitic slates and semipelitic schists. It has been suggested by Anderton (1985) that whereas in the east the tillite was formed below floating ice, the western outcrops were deposited from grounded ice. This accords with the palaeogeography of Anderton (1985), which shows the Appin Group sediments being deposited on the north-western edge of a gulf between the actively separating continents of Laurentia and Baltica.

The remainder of the Argyll Group comprises shallow-marine sediments characterised by cycles of basin deepening and filling (Anderton, 1985); these sediments are now metamorphosed to quartzites, grits, pelitic and semipelitic schists and subsidiary dolomites and marbles. At the top of the group, basic pillow lavas interbedded with metasediments form the Tayvallich Volcanics (Figure 22).

The boundary between the Appin and Argyll groups cannot be identified offshore, although it is tentatively suggested that, like the Appin Group, the Argyll Group may be largely continuous from Islay to Donegal. The group is also likely to form much of the offshore outcrop of the Highland Border Ridge (Figure 14). In north-eastern Islay, Jura, and along the Argyll coast with its many islands, the Dalradian is represented by the Argyll Group, and the offshore outcrop in this region is taken to belong to the same group. On Islay and Jura, the metasediments are heavily intruded by epidiorite dykes. To the east, in the Sound of Jura, topographic data suggest that the Skervuile Ridge, like adjacent islands off Jura, is formed of Dalradian metasediments which also show a high density of dykes (Evans et al., 1980).

Southern Highland Group

The Southern Highland Group crops out in County Londonderry, County Antrim, Kintyre, Arran and the southern part of Argyll and Bute (Figure 14). It consists of turbiditic-fan sediments in the form of greywackes and slates, together with submarine volcanic rocks. The Southern Highland Group crops out in County Londonderry and extends offshore from Inishowen. In County Antrim, the

Southern Highland Group forms part of the Highland Border Ridge which runs from County Antrim to Argyll, although offshore in the North Channel it is largely overlain by younger sediments (Figure 14). In Kintyre, southern Argyll, and on Bute, the Southern Highland Group comprises phyllites, greywackes, and volcaniclastic units with abundant amphibolite sheets. These have been extrapolated to submarine outcrops off the Mull of Kintyre, in Kilbrannan Sound, and at the mouth of Loch Fyne. The boundary between the Southern Highland and the Argyll groups is probably displaced in Loch Fyne by the Sound of Bute Fault (BGS Clyde Solid Geology sheet).

Colonsay and Bowmore groups

It was Stewart (1975) who first proposed these lithostratigraphical units. The Colonsay Group lies to the west of the Loch Gruinart Fault and forms the islands of Colonsay, Oronsay and north-western Islay, whereas the Bowmore Group crops out only to the east of the Loch Gruinart Fault on Islay. Both groups were originally considered to be Torridonian (Wilkinson, 1907).

Following examination of structural and lithological evidence, a tentative correlation of the Colonsay Group with Appin Group Dalradian metasediments was made (Stewart and Hackman, 1973; Stewart, 1975). Later, Fitches and Maltman (1984) identified a first phase of deformation in the Colonsay Group that may be of late Proterozoic age. The uncertainty of the timing of this phase, together with lack of evidence on the nature of pre-Permian movement on the Loch Gruinart Fault, means that the age of this group must still be regarded as enigmatic. The offshore extent of the Colonsay Group is uncertain, although possibly related samples of siltstone, phyllite, sandstone and conglomerate have been recovered from the sea bed some 10 km to the west of Islay, and between Islay and Colonsay (BGS Malin Solid Geology sheet).

Fitches and Maltman (1984) were, however, able to use tectonic similarities to correlate the Bowmore Group with the upper part of the Argyll Group to the east, from which it is separated by the Loch Skerrols Thrust (Figure 4). In particular, a south-easterly dipping cleavage found in both sequences is interpreted as Caledonian in age. They cite the lithological similarity between the coarse-grained sandstones of the Bowmore Group and the Crinan Grit Formation as additional evidence for this correlation. The offshore outcrop of the Bowmore Group is very restricted (BGS Malin Solid Geology sheet).

CAMBRIAN TO SILURIAN

The white to buff, Cambro-Ordovician quartzites and other sedimentary rocks which occur on the north-western mainland of Scotland and Skye have not been identified offshore. It is presumed that they extend north from Loch Eriboll near the line of the Moine Thrust (e.g. Brewer and Smythe, 1984), and that they perhaps also occur south of Skye.

Late Cambrian to mid-Ordovician sedimentary and igneous rocks, termed the Highland Border Complex (Henderson and Robertson, 1982), are present in narrow wedges along the Highland Boundary Fault in central Scotland. They are distinguished from the Dalradian to the north on both lithological and structural grounds. The complex comprises both deep-sea and shallow-marine sedimentary rocks such as chert, mudstones, sandstones and limestones, as well as basic volcanic and intrusive rocks. Ultrabasic rocks, generally altered to serpentinite, also form an important part of the sequence. Offshore in the report area, rocks of the Highland Border Complex may occur in the northern Firth of Clyde region.

South of the Southern Upland Fault, sedimentary and subsidiary volcanic rocks of Ordovician to Silurian age form the Southern Uplands. They comprise mainly greywackes and shales deposited as paralic sediments on the north-western margin of the Iapetus Ocean. In the report area, rocks of Ordovician age, including the Ballantrae Complex, crop out at the coast north of the Southern Upland Fault (Figure 14). These are thought to extend offshore to be overlain by, or faulted against, Permo-Triassic sediments; no offshore basement samples have been obtained (BGS Clyde Solid Geology sheet).

GRANITES

The intrusion of granitic magmas into the crust occurred throughout the Caledonian orogeny. In Scotland, the peak of Grampian tectonothermal events is marked by the emplacement of an apparent S-type granitoid at 590 ± 2 Ma (Rogers et al., 1989). However, the main episode of granitic magmatism occurred between 435 and 390 Ma (Brown, 1983). Two representatives of the late- to post-kinematic suite of granitoid plutons at Strontian, and on the Ross of Mull, have coastal exposures, and both extend offshore (Figures 3 and 14). The Strontian pluton probably extends for only a very short distance offshore out to the Great Glen fault zone in Loch Linnhe. Rocks ascribed to the Ross of Mull granite have been recovered farther offshore (Barber et al., 1979). Samples of quartz-mica diorite, granodiorite and tonalite around the Torran Rocks suggest that the pluton, or related intrusive rocks, extends some 15 km south-west from the Ross of Mull.

A low circular Bouguer gravity anomaly over the Islay–Donegal Platform (Malin Bouguer Anomaly sheet) has been tentatively interpreted as representing a buried granitic mass of unknown age (BGS Malin Solid Geology sheet). Farther west, the granitic Malin Complex (Riddihough, 1968; Riddihough and Young, 1971) on the line of the Great Glen fault system is also of unspecified age, although it may well be post-Mesozoic (Evans et al., 1980). Off the coast of Donegal, the extent of the late Caledonian Thorr and Fanad plutons of the Donegal Granite Complex (Pitcher and Berger, 1972) has been mapped (Evans and Whittington, 1976; BGS Malin Solid Geology sheet).

4 Devonian (Old Red Sandstone)

By the end of the Caledonian orogeny in late Silurian to Early Devonian times, a mountainous belt extended from what is now the eastern part of the American continent to Spitzbergen. This resulted in an extensive area of continental deposition that covered much of present-day Britain, Scandinavia and Greenland. In Britain, particularly in the Midland Valley of Scotland, Northumberland and south-western England, sedimentation was accompanied by volcanism that was characterised by the extrusion of calc-alkaline, intermediate, basic and acidic lavas.

The Devonian sediments of the British Isles fall into two main facies, marine and continental. The marine facies is present only in south-western England and the south of Ireland, on the southern fringe of the newly created Pangaean continent. The continental facies to the north is commonly termed the Old Red Sandstone (ORS); this extended over all other parts of the UK and Ireland, including the Midland Valley and other districts in and around the report area.

The lithostratigraphical term 'Old Red Sandstone' is sometimes used synonymously with the Devonian, with a similar tripartite division (Figure 23), although the ORS facies includes rocks of both late Silurian and Early Carboniferous age (Paterson and Hall, 1986). However, there is only sparse biostratigraphical age control, for this facies is dominantly formed of barren, red sandstones, mudstones and conglomerates laid down in a largely semiarid, terrestrial environment. Furthermore, any fish remains and spores present are commonly difficult to correlate with the faunas and floras of the contemporary marine environment.

Thick sequences of ORS sediments and lavas occur within the Midland Valley. Late Silurian to Early Devonian conglomerates and sandstones of the Lower ORS were laid down on a dominantly westward-dipping palaeoslope. The source areas were the Scottish Highlands to the north, and the Southern Uplands to the south. Middle Devonian sediments are absent in the Midland Valley, for this was a time of uplift and erosion in that region. However, in north-east Scotland, Orkney and offshore to the north of Scotland, Middle ORS sediments form the greater part of the Orcadian Lake succession (Mykura, 1983; Andrews et al., 1990). Following uplift in the Midland Valley, a change to eastward sediment transport is indicated by palaeocurrent directions in the Upper ORS sediments (Paterson et al., 1990), opposite to that in the Lower Devonian rocks.

In the Malin–Hebrides area, ORS strata are found mainly in and around the Firth of Clyde and Northern Ireland (Figure 24). They form a discontinuous band from Greenock through Arran and Kintyre to Cushendall in Northern Ireland, and are present in southern Ayrshire. There is also a large outcrop of lavas with sediments to the south of the Great Glen Fault around Oban and in the Firth of Lorne. Further isolated outcrops of sediments are found within the Great Glen fault zone to the north-east. Farther north, Coward et al. (1989) tentatively inferred the presence of Devonian sediments at depth in the North Minch Basin, but the results of well 156/17-1, which drilled from Permo-Triassic directly into Torridonian, make this unlikely.

On shallow-seismic sections, the ORS is identified as a largely featureless seismic unit with a few weak internal reflectors beneath a moderately strongly reflecting top. The lacus-

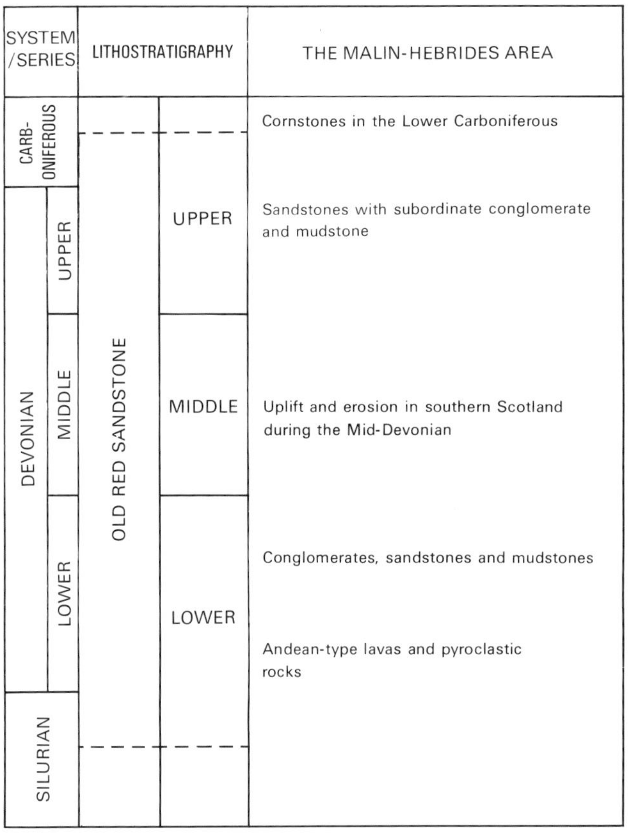

Figure 23 Devonian lithostratigraphy in the report area.

trine sediments of the Orcadian Basin locally produce clearer internal reflectors, but there is no evidence of this facies in the Malin–Hebrides area. In some cases, the seismic texture may be indistinguishable from that of the Torridonian or other basement rocks, and the redbed lithology may commonly be similar to that of the Torridonian and the Permo-Triassic. The prime criterion for interpretation is therefore extrapolation from the better-understood onshore sections. In this context it is interesting to note that the Stornoway Formation, which can be viewed in detail at land sections and is now considered to be of Permo-Triassic age (Steel and Wilson, 1975), had previously been attributed to both the Torridonian (Jehu and Craig, 1934) and the Devonian (Kürsten, 1957), as well as to the Permo-Triassic (Stevens, 1914). Considering that such problems arise on land, it is not surprising that identification of the offshore redbeds is necessarily tentative.

FIRTH OF LORNE AND THE GREAT GLEN FAULT ZONE

The Lorne Plateau to the east of Oban is dominated by a sequence of Early Devonian lavas erupted contemporaneously with the calc-alkaline plutonic activity which distinguishes the region. The lava pile consists mainly of andesitic and basaltic flows, with subordinate dacites, rhyolites, and minor tuff layers (Roberts, 1966). Near Oban and on the island of

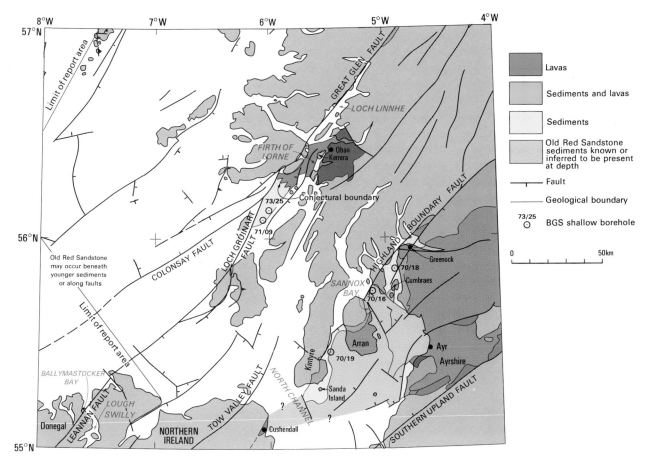

Figure 24 Distribution of Devonian sediments and lavas. No Devonian rocks are known in the northern part of the report area.

Kerrera (Figure 24), there are ORS conglomerates, sandstones and mudstones of fluvial origin resting on a basal breccia, the clasts of which are predominantly derived from the underlying Dalradian slates. In the Firth of Lorne, a fault-bounded block of ORS sediments and lavas is interpreted as an offshore extension of the outcrop at Oban and on Kerrera.

In the north-eastern part of the Firth of Lorne outcrop, the Lower ORS cover is thought to be discontinuous and composed of altered intermediate and basic lavas (BGS Argyll Solid Geology sheet). Several sea-bed samples collected from this area include olivine basalt and altered, porphyritic, hornblende andesite (Barber et al., 1979). To the south-west, the rocks are mainly conglomerates and pebbly sandstones. Borehole 71/09, at the southern end of this outcrop (Figure 24), penetrated 11 m of well-indurated, purplish red sandstone with interbedded, fine-grained, partly micaceous sandstones and well-defined pebbly sandstone layers; the pebbles are mainly of quartzite, some showing slight foliation. This sediment has been assigned to the Lower ORS.

Borehole 73/25, some 7 km to the north, penetrated 4 m of red sandstone similar to the fine-grained sediments in borehole 71/09, but less well indurated and brighter orange in colour. Blackbourn (1981) attempted to identify ages of Scottish redbeds by examining their colour; Devonian sediments are in general more purplish, and Mesozoic sediments nearer to brick red. Both colour and palynological analysis of the very limited miospores from borehole 73/25 suggest a Late Triassic to Early Jurassic age. However, the seismic texture and general pattern of outcrop in the area are both at variance with this determination and indicative of the ORS. The core may indeed be of early Mesozoic age, but the out-

crop is probably either of very limited extent or forms only a thin cover.

The Firth of Lorne outcrop is bounded to the north-west by the Colonsay and Loch Gruinart faults which, together with the Dubh Artach Fault, represent the extension of the Great Glen fault system south-westwards from Mull. ORS outcrops are recorded elsewhere in the vicinity of the Great Glen Fault; Stoker (1982) described one such outlier on the northern shore of Loch Linnhe where both the presence of coarse-grained scree breccias and early deformation of the sequence suggest active penecontemporaneous tectonism within the Great Glen fault zone. In Donegal, Lower Devonian sediments crop out adjacent to the Leannan Fault at Ballymastocker Bay (Figure 24), where 250 m of sandstone and conglomerate overlie a basal conglomerate which contains clasts of local Dalradian provenance (Holland, 1981). These sediments may extend under Lough Swilly (Evans, 1974), and other isolated occurrences of ORS sediment could be present anywhere along these major faults.

THE FIRTH OF CLYDE TO NORTHERN IRELAND

The most extensive outcrop of Devonian rocks in the report area occurs in the Firth of Clyde region (Figure 24). The main onshore outcrop is found to the south-east of the Highland Boundary Fault, although the ORS locally oversteps northwards across it. Along this Highland border zone, ORS conglomerates interbedded with sandstones are up to 4000 m thick in the west, where there are indications of contemporaneous fault movement. Many of the large clasts are well rounded, and Bluck (1978) suggested that these were derived from the Highland area to the north, which was itself an area of conglomerate deposition during the Early Devonian. Indeed, the Lower ORS is believed to have rested unconformably on an erosional surface substantially similar to that now present in the Highlands (Bluck, 1984). No Middle ORS is present, and the Upper ORS sediments are predominantly sandstones which pass up without significant break into Lower Carboniferous sandstones with cornstones. The cornstones, which represent ancient caliche soil horizons, are present mainly in the south-western part of this outcrop.

Faulting in the upper Firth of Clyde near to the Highland Boundary Fault has resulted in a complex outcrop pattern north of the Cumbraes, where the offshore geology is largely extrapolated from the onshore sections. Two offshore boreholes (Figure 24) have drilled unfossiliferous sediments interpreted as ORS facies. Borehole 70/16 penetrated 1 m of fine-grained, well-sorted, quartzose, red sandstone with greenish reduction spots and lenses of conglomerate containing clasts of quartz and siltstone. Borehole 70/18 recovered 4 m of similar, fine- to medium-grained, moderately sorted sandstone.

On Arran, both Lower and Upper ORS sediments are present as a condensed sequence up to 2000 m thick lying unconformably on Dalradian schists. North-east of Arran, the ORS of Sannox Bay may be traced offshore, where its outcrop terminates against the Permo-Triassic at the Brodick Bay Fault (Figures 13 and 24). The ORS is however thought to be present at depth between Arran and the Cumbraes (BGS Clyde Solid Geology sheet). South-west of Arran, an outcrop of undivided ORS can be traced along the north-eastern flank of the South-West Arran Trough to the east coast of Kintyre (Figures 13 and 24), where both Lower and Upper ORS occur on land. In this outcrop, borehole 70/19 penetrated 4 m of coarse-grained conglomerate composed of large cobbles and boulders of volcanic rock in a sandstone matrix that is carbonate cemented; the rock has the appear-

ance of 'Basal Lower Old Red Sandstone' (Deegan, 1978). It is probably similar to the Lower ORS sediments on Kintyre, or to those on Arran (Deegan, 1978) where andesitic boulders have been observed (Macgregor, 1965). Little or no trace of the Highland Boundary Fault has been found either in this area or farther south, where the ORS outcrop of south-east Kintyre extends offshore around Sanda Island (Figure 24). To the south and east, the ORS is overlain unconformably by Permian and Triassic sediments (Figure 3), but geophysical interpretations suggest that thick ORS sequences are present at depth (Dobinson, 1978; McLean and Deegan, 1978).

In eastern Northern Ireland at Cushendall, 900 m of ORS sediments and lavas rest unconformably on Dalradian schists, the lowermost beds being massive conglomerates with a large proportion of quartzite boulders (Wilson, 1972). The offshore extent of the Cushendall outcrop is unknown, but is probably very limited as it is overlain by Permo-Triassic sediment in the North Channel Basin. The ORS is likely to be present beneath the North Channel (Figure 24), although perhaps thinning rapidly to the west (BGS Clyde Solid Geology sheet).

South of Ayr, an outcrop of Lower ORS sediments and andesites may be traced up to 3 km offshore (Figure 24), where it is mapped as undifferentiated Devonian (BGS Clyde Solid Geology sheet). On land, the sequence comprises red conglomerates and sandstones interdigitating with basalt, andesite, dacite and rhyolite (Bluck, 1978). The conglomerates contain clasts of greywacke, chert and lava derived from the Southern Uplands, but clasts of quartzite are also present, suggesting derivation also from the Dalradian to the north and west. The offshore Devonian outcrop is faulted against the Permo-Triassic of the Carrick Basin (Figure 13), although it is believed to occur beneath the younger sediments in much of the Firth of Clyde region (McLean and Deegan, 1978).

5 Carboniferous

Continental deposition in the western Scottish area during the Devonian was followed in the Carboniferous by fluctuating marine and nonmarine sedimentation. This change coincided with the continued northward migration of the continents, and the concomitant climatic adjustment from an arid to a more-equatorial regime. The Scottish Highlands, Southern Uplands, Welsh Massif and London-Brabant Massif remained as positive topographic features, sometimes providing sources of sediment for the main depositional basins in southern England, the Midlands, the Northumberland Trough, the Midland Valley of Scotland and much of Ireland. In the Midland Valley of Scotland, frequent marine incursions during the Dinantian provided conditions suitable for the deposition of limestone and generally fine-grained clastic sediment (Figure 25). During the Silesian, nonmarine conditions were more common; initial fluvial sedimentation with some marine incursions gave way to delta complexes in which coal-bearing sediments were laid down.

Much of the Carboniferous sedimentation took place during syndepositional basin development. In some parts of the Midland Valley, up to 3000 m of Carboniferous rocks occur, whereas in others the succession is much thinner. Smythe (1989) has postulated that crustal extension, caused by plate-tectonic movement in the Arctic–North Atlantic region, was associated with the first phase of opening of the Rockall Trough. This gave rise to alkaline rift volcanism in the UK area (Ziegler, 1981), with the eruption of basic lavas and tuffs, and the emplacement of intrusive igneous bodies. Volcanism was widespread during the Dinantian, and again in Late Carboniferous to Early Permian times. The Carboniferous sequence is intruded by teschenitic dolerites of Late Carboniferous age and quartz-dolerites of Early Permian age; these intrusions are usually in the form of sills which can be as much as 150 m thick.

Around the Malin–Hebrides sea area, Carboniferous strata crop out in the eastern Firth of Clyde region, at Machrihanish in Kintyre, and in Northern Ireland. There is also a minor outlier at Morvern (Figure 26); these point to a more widespread original disposition of Carboniferous rocks than is suggested by the present outcrop pattern. Carboniferous rocks may well occur at depth in many parts of the report area; reworked Carboniferous miospores have been discovered in Jurassic sediments in the Little Minch (Binns et al., 1974b), and the presence of Carboniferous rocks has been inferred below the Permo-Triassic in the depositional basins in the north of the area (Stein, 1988).

On shallow-seismic profiles, the Carboniferous appears as a massive sequence with traces of bedding reflectors. The presence of intrusive bodies is marked by areas of strongly reflecting surfaces above zones of structureless seismic character. Highly reflective surfaces with numerous hyperbolic point-sources and diffraction patterns can be interpreted as the upper surfaces of shallow sills. In the Firth of Clyde region, a number of magnetic anomalies may be correlated with individual intrusive igneous bodies (McLean and Deegan, 1978).

SUB-SYSTEM	SERIES	MACHRIHANISH AND NORTHERN IRELAND	AYRSHIRE AND THE FIRTH OF CLYDE	DEPOSITIONAL ENVIRONMENT
SILESIAN	WESTPHALIAN	Sandstones, mudstones and coals	Lavas (upper Westphalian to Lower Permian)	Volcanic activity and shallow intrusions
			Sandstones, mudstones, coals (reddening of some sediments)	Delta complexes in subsiding basins
	NAMURIAN	Volcanics with sandstones, mudstones, limestones and coals	Sandstones, siltstones and mudstones with some coals	Fluvial (delta top) in locally subsiding basins
DINANTIAN	VISÉAN	Basalts and tuffs	Limestones with mudstones, siltstones and sandstones	Height of marine influence
		Interbedded conglomerates and sandstones		Basin subsidence
				Volcanic activity
		Basalts and tuffs	Basalts and tuffs with mudstones and cementstones	Lagoonal, brackish water
	TOURNAISIAN	Upper Old Red Sandstone		Semiarid desert

Figure 25 The Carboniferous rocks in and adjacent to the report area.

RATHLIN TROUGH AND ADJACENT OCCURRENCES

The Machrihanish Basin, to the east of the Rathlin Trough (Figure 26), is part of an Upper Palaeozoic outlier which contains strata of both Devonian and Carboniferous age. The onshore sequence comprises Devonian sandstones overlain by Dinantian, possibly Viséan, basalts. Namurian volcanics are interbedded with sandstones, mudstones, limestones and coals; these are overlain by a Westphalian clastic sedimentary sequence which includes several coal seams which have been worked commercially. This represents a complete but condensed sequence that is around 700 m thick compared with a maximum of 3000 m in the Midland Valley. The offshore extension of the Machrihanish Basin continues at outcrop for some 15 km to the west, where it is bounded by the Tow Valley Fault, which downthrows to the north-west. Within this outcrop, BGS borehole 73/03 penetrated 4 m of soft, white, coarse-grained sandstone described as a 'ganister' (Deegan, 1978) and interpreted as being of Carboniferous age.

In Northern Ireland, Carboniferous sediments and volcanic rocks crop out both near Ballycastle in County Antrim and in and around Lough Foyle to the west (Figure 26). To the east

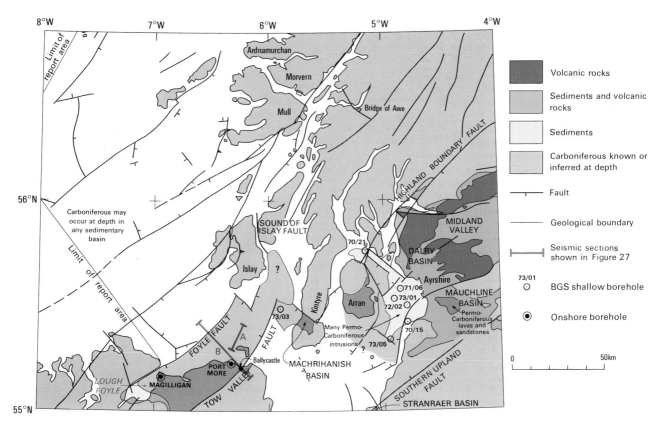

Figure 26 Distribution of Carboniferous sedimentary and volcanic rocks. No Carboniferous rocks have been proven in the northern part of the report area.

of Ballycastle on the Highland Border Ridge (Figure 4), a sequence of Viséan conglomerates and sandstones interdigitates with basaltic lavas and tuffs. These are overlain by further sandstones with thin coal seams, nonmarine and marine shale bands, and limestones of Viséan to Namurian age. The sequence is a condensed succession similar in many respects to that at Machrihanish (Wilson, 1972). The two areas of outcrop may be part of the same basin, structurally connected beneath the Permo-Triassic east of the Tow Valley Fault.

In and around Lough Foyle, sandstones, mudstones and thin coals of unspecified Carboniferous age comprise part of a discontinuous outcrop which persists southwards to Dungannon in County Tyrone (Sevastopulo, 1981). These sediments rest unconformably on Dalradian schists and are overlain by Permo-Triassic breccias and sandstones. The nearby Magilligan borehole (Figure 26 and see Figure 31) penetrated around 350 m of upper Viséan to lower Namurian sediments. Here, sandstones with grits and conglomerates pass upwards into sandstones with mudstones and thin coals and shales (Limavady 1:50 000 Solid Geology sheet 6). It is likely that the Lough Foyle Carboniferous sequence is of a similar age to that recovered in the Magilligan borehole. Evans et al. (1980), using gravity and deep-seismic reflection profiles, inferred the presence of up to 1000 m of Carboniferous rocks beneath the southern part of the Rathlin Trough (Figure 27).

To the west of the report area in the Donegal Basin, 949 m of Upper Carboniferous sediments with common volcaniclastic layers in the upper 60 m have been drilled in well 13/3-1 in the Irish sector (Tate and Dobson, 1989). This further attests to the possibly widespread distribution of Carboniferous strata below younger sediments over much of the southern part of the report area, including the Malin and Colonsay basins.

THE FIRTH OF CLYDE REGION

In Ayrshire, Carboniferous sedimentary and igneous rocks occur in the Dalry and Mauchline basins (Figure 26), where lavas and marine sediments of Dinantian to Namurian age are overlain by Westphalian Coal Measures. This sequence has been heavily intruded by dolerite sills and dykes of Late Carboniferous to Early Permian age, and, in the central part of the Mauchline Basin, is overlain by lavas and sandstone of late Westphalian to Early Permian age. To the west in Arran, Carboniferous strata become progressively thinner westwards and eventually pinch out; on the west coast of the island, Permo-Triassic sediments directly overlie Devonian sandstones.

Westward of the onshore part of the Mauchline Basin, the Carboniferous outcrop extends seawards from Ayrshire (Figure 26) before it is overlain by Permo–Triassic sediments (BGS Clyde Solid Geology sheet). The precise nature of the Permian–Carboniferous boundary is uncertain, and Upper Carboniferous to Permian lavas may occur offshore. Several BGS boreholes (Deegan, 1978) have been drilled in this area (Figure 26); the best sequence is from borehole 70/15, where 5 m of interbedded sandstone and marl were recovered. The sandstone beds are commonly very fine to fine grained and micaceous; they are reddish in colour, although one hard white sandstone with carbonaceous streaks has also been recorded. Some ripple bedding is present, and reduction spots are common. The interbedded marls are micaceous and partly sandy, dominantly red, but with green reduction spots. Borehole 73/01 penetrated 10 m of red marl with common greenish grey reduction spots; it is soft and micaceous near the top beneath Pleistocene till, but becomes harder below. The sediments contain well-preserved specimens of

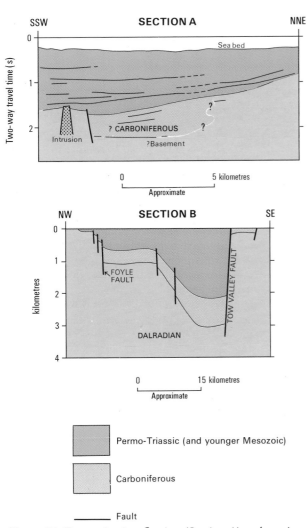

SECTION A
SSW   NNE
Sea bed
Intrusion
? CARBONIFEROUS
?Basement

0   5 kilometres
Approximate

SECTION B
NW   SE
FOYLE FAULT
TOW VALLEY FAULT
DALRADIAN

0   15 kilometres
Approximate

Permo-Triassic (and younger Mesozoic)

Carboniferous

Fault

Figure 27 Deep-seismic reflection (Section A) and gravity (Section B) interpretations of the Rathlin Trough. After Evans et al. (1980). Note difference in scales between the two sections. For locations see Figure 26.

Neuropteris scheuchzeri Hoffman, a seed-fern of late Westphalian age.

Borehole 72/02 recovered 3 m of hard, grey sandstone with ripple marks, overlying conglomeratic sandstone and mottled, greenish grey and reddish brown, silty mudstone. Borehole 71/06 recovered 5 m of finely laminated grey and purplish brown mudstone. Palaeontological examination has yielded several specimens of *Lycospora pusilla* (Ibrahim) Somers which is a common component of Carboniferous spore assemblages, but is not stratigraphically diagnostic at the stage level. Borehole 73/05 recovered washings of sandstone and coal interpreted as being of Carboniferous age.

Off the north-eastern coast of Arran, submarine outcrop of Carboniferous rocks is identified as a continuation of the Upper Palaeozoic rocks seen on land. Offshore, the Late Carboniferous sediments are mapped as extending across the line of the Highland Boundary Fault, although the precise relationships are difficult to determine. Borehole 70/21 recov-

ered 2 m of sandstone interbedded with marl and siltstone; the sandstone is fine to medium grained, grey or purplish grey, with green reduction spots and some intraformational rip-up clasts. The partly laminated and micaceous marl is pale green and calcareous, whereas the 'marly' siltstone is red with green reduction spots. The core is interpreted as Carboniferous in age, but there is no confirmatory miospore evidence.

The cores recovered in the Firth of Clyde suggest that much of the offshore Carboniferous comprises red sandstone and marl. The presence of reddening is common in the upper part of the Coal Measures in the Ayrshire Coalfield. Mykura (1960) recorded that not only are sediments reddened, but also that the bedding in mudstones becomes obscured by chemical reaction and that coals are chemically replaced by limestone. Mykura (1960) showed that these alterations are secondary, possibly through circulation of oxygenated groundwater. The extent of the Carboniferous beneath younger sediments is not defined, but interpretations in the South-West Arran Trough and the North Channel Basin indicate that the Permo-Triassic sediments rest directly on Devonian (McLean and Deegan, 1978), although Carboniferous rocks are present in the Stranraer Basin (Figure 26).

NORTHERN OCCURRENCES

North of Islay there are two outcrops of Carboniferous sediments and lavas on land (Figure 26). In Morvern, around 100 m of Upper Carboniferous sandstone with thin mudstone bands and coal seams are seen in the lower part of the cliff section at Inninmore Bay (Richey, 1961). Some Carboniferous plant remains have been identified, suggesting that these sediments are Westphalian Coal Measures. It is unlikely that the Carboniferous outcrop continues offshore for more than a few hundred metres, where it is believed to overlie Moine schists. Carboniferous sediments of similar lithology overlie the Early Devonian Lorne lavas in a very small outcrop near Bridge of Awe (Johnstone, 1966).

Upper Carboniferous miospores have been identified in samples obtained in the Little Minch (Eden et al., 1973; Binns et al., 1974b). These are considered to be reworked (Chesher et al., 1983), but their occurrence does at least suggest the former presence of Carboniferous strata nearby. Further indirect evidence for Carboniferous rocks in this region has been documented by Jehu and Craig (1934), who identified glacial erratics of Carboniferous age on the Outer Hebrides.

Stein (1988), in a structural interpretation of seismic-reflection data, suggested that over 500 m of Carboniferous strata may be present beneath Permo-Triassic and younger rocks in the Sea of the Hebrides–Little Minch Trough. Stein (1988) interpreted this limited evidence, together with Permo-Carboniferous dyke activity, to indicate that Late Palaeozoic sedimentary basins developed at a time of widespread extension coincident with the first phase of Rockall Trough rifting (cf. Smythe, 1989).

6 Permo-Triassic

The tensional tectonic regime initiated during Early Carboniferous rifting in the North Atlantic continued to influence basin development in Permian and Triassic times. Increased tectonic activity during the Late Carboniferous and Early Permian resulted in the emplacement of east–west-trending basic dykes in the Midland Valley of Scotland, and in Argyll (Francis, 1978; Speight and Mitchell, 1978; Upton, 1982). Extensive igneous activity took place in Northern Ireland, and in the Sound of Islay (Figure 26; Penn et al., 1983; Upton et al., 1987). The same tensional phase led to the evolution of largely westerly tilted half-grabens in a zone which may be traced from off the north coast of Scotland southwards to the Main Porcupine Basin west of Ireland (Tate and Dobson, 1989). Many of the faults forming the western margins of these asymmetrical basins were reactivated basement structures (Stein, 1988; Figure 28). The basins continued to develop during the Permian and Triassic, resulting in the deposition of a substantial thickness of sediment (Steel and Wilson, 1975).

Over much of Europe, including the North Sea and Irish Sea, the Permian and Triassic may be distinguished as distinct stratigraphical entities, but this is not possible in the report area due to lack of stratigraphical control. Both periods were characterised by arid climatic conditions, resulting in the deposition of continental redbed and evaporite sequences. This contrasts markedly with the wetter, equatorial climate experienced in the region during the Carboniferous. During the Early Permian, the development of isolated basins provided the loci for the deposition of redbeds (Ziegler, 1981), whereas during the Late Permian, the basins in the North Sea and Irish Sea were intermittently inundated by the Zechstein Sea. At Larne, some 15 km south of the report area, there are over 100 m of Late Permian halite overlying 21 m of dolomite and dolomitic limestone (Penn et al., 1983). During the Triassic, continental redbed sedimentation was again widespread over Britain and surrounding areas. In Scotland and off its west coast, only terrestrial redbeds are known to be present, although marine influence can be seen in Northern Ireland, where almost 500 m of Late Triassic halite was deposited south of the report area at Larne (Wilson, 1972).

The paucity of fossils in both the Permian and Triassic means that in much of the Malin–Hebrides area, rocks of these ages are normally classified as Permo-Triassic or 'New Red Sandstone'. The Permo-Triassic sediments vary from conglomerates and pebbly sandstones to siltstones and mudstones, with local development of cornstone layers. The environment of deposition was terrestrial, and included both aeolian and fluvial facies. Sediments of Permo-Triassic age occur only sporadically on land surrounding the area, usually preserved as thin beds in laterally restricted, unconformable outliers. This is in sharp contrast to the offshore Permo-Triassic, which occurs as thick sequences in the fault-bounded basins (Steel, 1971a; Evans at al., 1982). The syndepositional movement which commonly took place during the evolution of these Permo-Triassic basins provided an important control on sedimentation (Kirton and Hitchen, 1987; Earle et al., 1989).

The onshore exposures on the west coast of Scotland have been investigated by Steel (1971b; 1974a; 1977), who identified two major sedimentary facies: floodplain and alluvial fan. The outcrops generally contain sediments from both facies, and in many cases a sequence of dominantly floodplain de-

posits is overlain by alluvial-fan facies sediments, which may suggest a general increase in the incidence of syndepositional fault movement.

The floodplain facies deposits include cyclothems from both low- and high-sinuosity rivers. Both types are upward-fining and generally finer grained than the alluvial-fan deposits with which they are in several instances laterally equivalent. The coarse-grained basal portions of the cyclothems commonly overlie an erosion surface, and minor amounts of conglomerate which locally occur in these basal portions show no correlation between maximum clast size and bed thickness. Abundant cornstone profiles are better developed in the low-sinuosity river deposits, indicating long periods of subaerial exposure and soil development (Steel, 1974b). High-sinuosity channels generally succeed low-sinuosity channels, possibly indicating a reduction in source-area relief, and perhaps a climatic change to less-arid conditions.

The alluvial-fan sediments are divided into mudflow, streamflood and braided-stream deposits. The mudflow and streamflood deposits are dominantly conglomeratic with locally derived pebbles, although the streamflood sediments tend to be better sorted and are marked by large-scale cross-stratification. The braided-stream deposits are better sorted than both the other facies, and are generally finer grained. Steel (1971b) was able to correlate maximum grain size with bed thickness, showing that the best correlation is in the mudflow facies, implying rapid burial with little erosion and reworking.

Offshore, differentiation of these facies proves problematic. Indeed, it can even be difficult to distinguish Permo-Triassic from Devonian and Torridonian redbeds. Work by Blackbourn (1981) on the colour of reddened sandstones shows that Mesozoic sediments are in general brick red, whereas the Devonian is more purplish in colour. In addition, the younger sediments tend to be the more friable, the Torridonian sandstones and arkoses being in places highly indurated.

Shallow-seismic surveys provide the major source of offshore information, but where there is little or no stratigraphical control, many basins have been described merely as Permian to Cretaceous in age. In such cases, subdivision on the grounds of seismic signature is not considered possible, for both the Permo-Triassic and younger Mesozoic rocks are generally seen as reflective beds. The Permo-Triassic may be distinguished from the Torridonian by the absence of internal reflectors and the generally more rugged topography of the latter. On deep-seismic sections, the base of the Permo-Triassic is commonly poorly defined.

NORTH LEWIS AND NORTH MINCH BASINS

A thick section of Permo-Triassic occurs onshore on Lewis (Figure 28), where Steel (1971a) identified 600 m of braided-stream deposits overlain by a further 600 m of conglomeratic mudflow-facies sediments. This sequence lies unconformably upon, or is faulted against, the Lewisian (Lovell, 1983). The red sandstones and conglomerates contain no diagnostic fossils, and have been termed the 'Stornoway Formation' (Stewart, 1969), though Warrington et al. (1980) recommended that this term should not be formally accepted. Steel and Wilson (1975), in a detailed sedimentological inter-

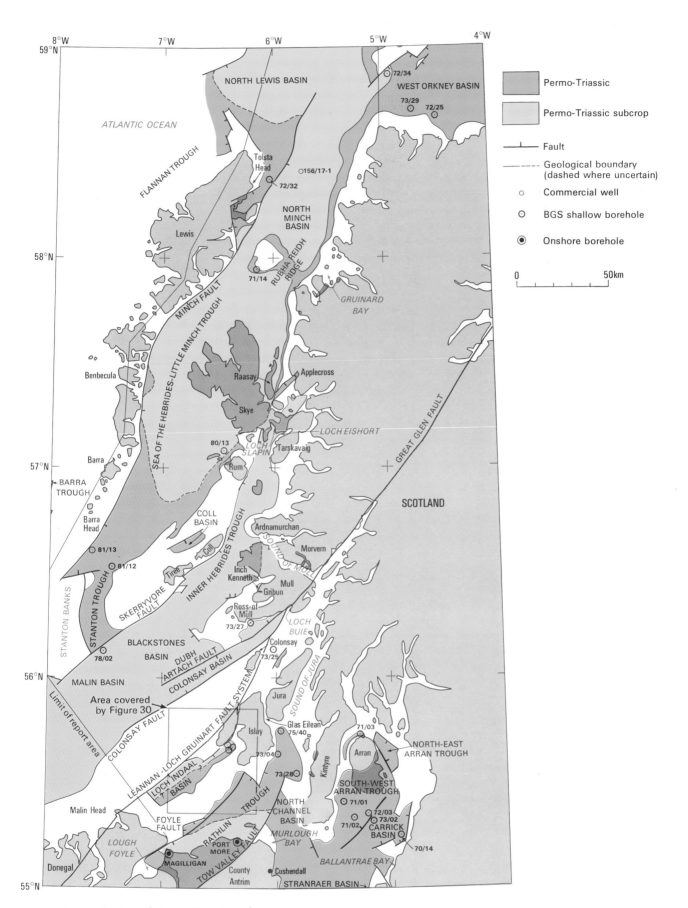

Figure 28 Distribution of Permo-Triassic rocks.

33

pretation, identified both alluvial-fan and floodplain facies in the formation. The alluvial-fan facies comprises conglomerates and sandstones with thin impersistent siltstones, and is divided into mudflow, streamflood and braided-stream deposits. The floodplain deposits are finer grained.

The Stornoway Formation was originally correlated by Geikie (1878) with the 'Cambrian Conglomerate' of mainland Scotland, although he noted that the Stornoway sandstones were in general less 'coherent' than the mainland outcrops of the Torridonian. Peach and Horne (1930) were probably the first to suggest a Mesozoic age, though this was not generally accepted by contemporary workers. Jehu and Craig (1934) provided a detailed description of the outcrop of the Stornoway Beds, and advocated a Torridonian age based on the thickness of the beds and their similarity to the Diabaig Group exposed on the Scottish mainland. Kürsten (1957) proposed a Devonian age, based on the premise that they were deposited after the main phase of thrusting, and that their thickness was more suggestive of the Old Red Sandstone than the Permo-Triassic.

The Stornoway Formation is now considered to be of Permo-Triassic age. Evidence for this assertion came from Steel (1971a), who compared the sequence with other Permo-Triassic sequences on Skye, Raasay and Mull, and at Gruinard Bay. He dismissed Kürsten's (1957) argument based on consideration of thickness, and suggested that the sequence shows

an overall thickening into The Minch. Studies of the sedimentology, carbonate content and pebble provenance, led to the abandonment of the Torridonian hypothesis. Palaeomagnetic work (Storetvedt and Steel, 1977) has provided the main evidence for a post-Devonian age; samples from the Stornoway Formation give a magnetic pole which corresponds closely with the European Late Permian pole.

The Stornoway Formation may therefore be regarded as the onshore continuation of the Permo-Triassic in the North Lewis Basin, the development of which, to the west of the Minch Fault (Figure 11), was partly controlled by the relaxation of former thrust planes (BGS Lewis Solid Geology sheet). Permo-Triassic rocks crop out in the southern part of the basin (Figure 28), and also to the west of Lewis where the basin extends towards the Flannan Trough. BGS borehole 72/32, off Tolsta Head, penetrated 8 m of soft, brick-red, very fine- to fine-grained sandstone displaying some traces of cross-bedding in an otherwise structureless sequence. This sediment is interpreted as Permo-Triassic on lithological grounds, and perhaps correlates with the floodplain facies of the Stornoway Formation.

Permo-Triassic sediments are also found in the North Minch Basin, which is separated from the North Lewis Basin by the Minch Fault (Figure 28). In the deepest part of the basin, up to 3000 m of Permo-Triassic sediments may occur in the hanging wall of the Minch Fault (Figure 11). These are

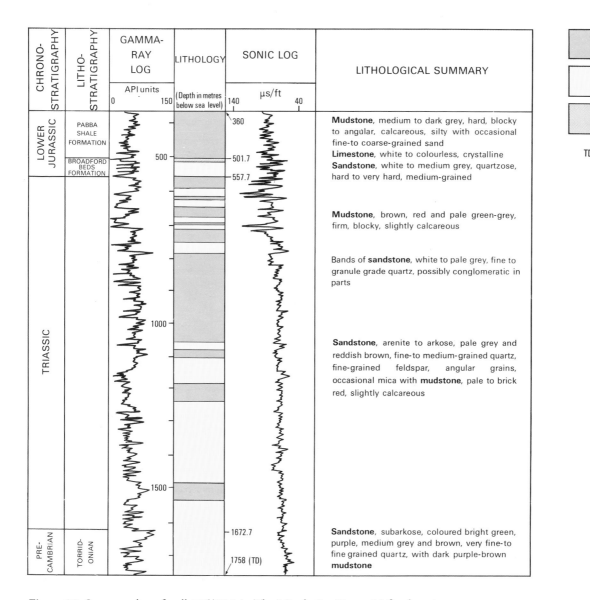

Figure 29 Summary log of well 156/17-1 in The Minch. See Figure 28 for location.

mainly covered by Lower Jurassic mudstones, but the Permo-Triassic crops out on the eastern and southern margins of the basin. Although the redbed nature of these sediments has been proven to the north of the Scottish coast (Evans et al., 1982), the first demonstration of Permo-Triassic rocks in the North Minch Basin came from well 156/17-1, which proved 1115 m of Permo-Triassic sandstone, siltstone and mudstone overlying Torridonian sandstone (Figure 29). The sediments, which are dominantly red but with subordinate green and grey reduced layers, include minor conglomerates and anhydrite. The sandstone is a generally fine- to very fine-grained quartz, with some feldspar. It is partly calcareous and has a low porosity.

There is a small occurrence of Permo-Triassic rocks on land to the south-west of Gruinard Bay (Figure 28), and in the south of the basin, Permo-Triassic rocks crop out on the flanks of the Rubha Reidh Ridge. On its southern flank, BGS borehole 71/14, recovered 16 m of barren, fine- to coarse-grained, red sandstone. The rock is in part conglomeratic, and has greyish green reduction patches associated with thin marl layers.

SEA OF THE HEBRIDES–LITTLE MINCH TROUGH

South of the Rubha Reidh Ridge, the Sea of the Hebrides–Little Minch Trough contains up to 1000 m of Permo-Triassic sediments (BGS Little Minch Solid Geology sheet). The trough is bounded to the west by the Minch Fault, and to the south and east its sediments lie unconformably upon, and are in part faulted against, Lewisian and Torridonian basement. Over much of this basin, particularly in the north, the Permo-Triassic is overlain by later Mesozoic sediments.

Outcrop of Permo-Triassic, however, continues southwards along the eastern margin of the basin from the Rubha Reidh Ridge to Raasay (Figure 28). The outcrop apparently becomes slightly narrower as the succession becomes thinner, although the boundary between the Permo-Triassic and the overlying Jurassic is poorly defined. On Raasay, a 65 m-thick Permo-Triassic section has been recorded by Steel (1971b), and both alluvial-fan and floodplain facies can be identified. As Steel (1971b) was unable to identify either the top or the base of this section, it is likely that it represents part of a rather thicker sequence.

The southern limit of Jurassic and younger cover in the trough is ill defined, but Permo-Triassic sediments have been recovered at sea bed, or beneath Quaternary deposits, in the south (Figure 28). Two rock samples east of Benbecula have yielded miospore assemblages of Late Permian and Rhaetian age (Binns et al., 1974b). Farther south near the Minch Fault, BGS borehole 81/13 penetrated 3.5 m of unfossiliferous red mudstone, sandstone and conglomerate, including a number of upward-fining units in which the finer-grained parts show current ripples and flame structures. Regional lithological relationships suggest that this sequence is Triassic in age, probably of the floodplain facies.

In the central part of the basin, the Mesozoic sediments are overlain by Tertiary basalts whose onshore outcrop forms much of the Isle of Skye. Between these basalts and the Torridonian of southern Skye and Rum, lies a band of Mesozoic sediments. These are exposed on Skye on the north coast of Soay Sound, where Permo-Triassic sandstones and conglomerates underlie Triassic sediments. Permo-Triassic conglomerates and sandstones also crop out on the northwest coast of the island of Rum. Within the offshore outcrop, borehole 80/13 drilled sediments of Early Jurassic age, suggesting that, for the most part, the Permo-Triassic is overlain by later Mesozoic sediments.

STANTON TROUGH AND COLL BASIN

To the south of the Sea of the Hebrides–Little Minch Trough, sediments of the Stanton Trough are faulted against the Lewisian of the Stanton Banks to the west. They lie unconformably upon, and are locally faulted against, the Lewisian of the Skerryvore Bank to the east (Figure 28). The northern limit of the Stanton Trough lies at an unconformable boundary where the Permo-Triassic of the Sea of the Hebrides–Little Minch Trough overlies sediments of the Stanton Trough. This unconformity can be seen as a distinct feature on shallow-seismic records, and was the chief evidence for the sediments in the Stanton Trough being considered as Torridonian by Binns et al. (1974b) and Evans et al. (1980; 1982). A Permo-Triassic age for this basin is now suggested in the light of more recent evidence from a sea-bed sample within the Stanton Trough (BGS Tiree Solid Geology sheet) and from BGS borehole 81/12 (Figure 28). This borehole recovered 5 m of very fine- to fine-grained, silty sandstone which although dominantly dark brownish red, is partly reduced to pale green. The colour of these beds (Blackbourn, 1981), and the presence of variable induration and several friable zones, implies a Permo-Triassic age.

North-east of the Stanton Trough, and to the north-west of the island of Coll, a small, unsampled basin has been identified lying across the boundary between the Torridonian and the Lewisian of the Skerryvore Bank (Figure 28). This has been named the Coll Basin, and is identified from its relatively low-lying topography and its north-westerly dipping reflectors. These features distinguish the basin from the rugged surrounding terrain which is internally structureless on seismic-reflection profiles. The position of the south-western margin is however uncertain, as the Torridonian has little relief locally, and the supposed younger sediments there lack seismic structure. The basin may contain up to 500 m of sediments that have been tentatively ascribed to the Permo-Triassic (BGS Tiree Solid Geology sheet).

West of the report area, some 30 km west of Barra Head (Figure 28), lies the Barra Trough, a largely faulted outlier resting on the Lewisian. The Permo-Triassic age originally postulated for the sediments of the basin (BGS Peach Solid Geology sheet) has been confirmed by BGS borehole 90/16, which drilled 13.15 m of reddish brown, fine- to very coarse-grained sandstone in the youngest sediments of the basin.

INNER HEBRIDES TROUGH

East of Rum, Coll and Tiree lies the Inner Hebrides Trough, which contains up to 1500 m of sediments (BGS Tiree Solid Geology sheet). Along its western margin on Skye, around 50 m of Triassic sandstones and conglomerates are seen near Loch Eishort and at Loch Slapin, where they unconformably overlie Torridonian sandstones and Cambrian limestones respectively (Steel, 1971b; Nicholson, 1978). The evidence of both the onshore geology and two offshore boreholes that have proved Jurassic rocks, suggest that the Permo-Triassic is likely to crop out only at the extreme eastern margin of the northern part of the basin. Mesozoic outcrop in the northern Inner Hebrides Trough is separated from its southern extension by an overlying sequence of Tertiary basalts (Figure 3). The Mesozoic rocks of the southern area are also considered to be mostly Jurassic at surface, with Permo-Triassic sediments cropping out only in the east.

At Gribun on Mull and on Inch Kenneth, Permo-Triassic conglomerates, sandstones and mudstones lie unconformably on the Moine. These sediments include what Steel (1974a) has identified as playa-lake deposits occurring near or beyond the toes of alluvial fans. Outcrops of Permo-Triassic in Ardnamurchan, Morvern and on the eastern coast of Mull cannot be correlated with the offshore geology, but indicate that deposition was probably more widespread than is indicated by the present basin configuration. There may be some Permo-Triassic sediment cover on the Moine in the Sound of Mull, but such cover is unlikely to be extensive (BGS Argyll Solid Geology sheet). These occurrences illustrate the contrast between the sequences with reduced thicknesses which are typical of onshore outcrops, and the thick sequences developed in the offshore basins.

COLONSAY AND MALIN BASINS

South of the Inner Hebrides Trough, the Dubh Artach Fault forms the northern boundary of the Colonsay Basin, which contains around 3000 m of Permian and Mesozoic sediments (BGS Tiree Solid Geology sheet). To the south-east, these sediments are faulted against Devonian and older rocks by the Colonsay Fault, which, like the Dubh Artach Fault, is considered to be a south-westerly extension of the Great Glen fault system. To the north-east, the sediments are overlain by basalt and cut by the Mull igneous intrusive complex. Associated with the Great Glen Fault at Loch Buie on Mull are Permo-Triassic alluvial-fan conglomerates. To the north of the Dubh Artach Fault, on the periphery of the basin near to where the Mesozoic strata overlap the Moine of the Ross of Mull, borehole 73/27 penetrated 2.25 m of fine-grained, greenish sandstone, tentatively ascribed to the Permo-Triassic. Within the basin, surface samples (Barber et al., 1979) provide Jurassic ages, so that, as in many of these Mesozoic basins, the presence of Permo-Triassic sediments at depth can only be inferred.

Between Colonsay and Jura, there is a small unsampled occurrence of inferred Permo-Triassic sediments (BGS Argyll Solid Geology sheet) downthrown to the north-west at a fault running parallel to the Loch Gruinart Fault. Sediments in nearby BGS borehole 73/25 have been dated as Late Triassic to Early Jurassic, and may be part of a patchy Permo-Triassic cover east of Colonsay.

To the west, beyond the outcrop of Tertiary sediments (Figures 3 and 28), lies the Malin Basin (Dobson and Whittington, 1992). In the northern part of this basin, near to the Skerryvore Fault, BGS borehole 78/02 drilled Jurassic sediments on the flank of a small syncline. Although Jurassic and later Mesozoic sediments may be found at the surface over much of the basin, regional considerations suggest that these overlie Permo-Triassic sediments which may be up to 2000 m thick (BGS Tiree Solid Geology sheet). To the south-east, the boundary between the Malin Basin and the Islay–Donegal Platform is partly defined by the Colonsay Fault, but to the south-west, Mesozoic sediments overlie the line of the fault. If this basin follows the regional structural pattern, Permo-Triassic rocks may form rockhead in the south-east of this basin, although perhaps only beyond the western limit of the report area.

Well 12/13-1, drilled in the Donegal Basin 135 km west-north-west of Malin Head, penetrated around 700 m of Late Permian to Rhaetian sediments (Tate and Dobson, 1989) comprising red, fine-to coarse-grained sandstone and mudstone interbedded with dolomite, limestone and anhydrite. Above this undifferentiated unit lie some 60 m of red-brown, calcareous mudstone and dolomite interpreted as Rhaetian from biostratigraphical data.

LOCH INDAAL BASIN AND RATHLIN TROUGH

South-east of the Islay-Donegal Platform (Figure 4), the Leannan–Loch Gruinart fault system forms the north-western limit of the Loch Indaal Basin, where up to 2500 m of Permo-Triassic sediments occur (Evans et al., 1980). These sediments onlap the Middle Bank, providing a fine example of the asymmetrical fault-bounded basins characteristic of the Malin–Hebrides area (Figure 30). Although Jurassic rocks are identified at rockhead in the north-eastern part of this basin, it is anticipated that much of the outcrop in the south-east is of Permo-Triassic age, as identified in BGS boreholes drilled in the outer part of Loch Indaal in the north of the basin (Figure 30).

In borehole 75/42, 20 m of barren, reddish brown mudstone with some coarse-grained sandstone beds are interpreted as being Permo-Triassic. The abundance of gypsum in these sediments may indicate marine influence during deposition. In borehole 75/41, which is higher in the sequence, 16 m of possibly Carnian to Norian gypsiferous mudstone of the Mercia Mudstone Group are overlain by 18.5 m of dark grey, well-laminated, fossiliferous mudstone yielding the diagnostic bivalve *Rhaetavicula contorta* Portlock and the palynomorphs *Ovalipollis pseudoalatus* (Thiergart) Schuurman, *Riccisporites tuberculatus* Lundblad, and *Rhaetipollis germanicus* Schultz. The fauna and microflora identify the mudstone as the Rhaetian Westbury Formation of the Penarth Group. This is the most northerly proven occurrence of the youngest part of the Mercia Mudstone Group and Westbury Formation in Britain. In England, this succession represents a transgressive phase that established the marine conditions which persisted into the later Mesozoic (Warrington, 1981; Warrington and Ivimey-Cook, 1990). Boreholes 75/43 and 75/44 penetrated Lias mudstone, allowing the Triassic–Jurassic boundary to be drawn with some certainty in the northern part of the basin (Figure 30).

To the south-east, the sediments of the Rathlin Trough are seen to extend north-west of the Foyle Fault and onlap the Middle Bank. The presence of possible Permian sediments (Pringle, 1947) preserved within a solution hollow in Dalradian limestone at Port nan Gallon on The Oa, Islay (Figure 30) implies that the Middle Bank may originally have been covered by Permo-Triassic sediments. Evans et al. (1980) postulated a maximum thickness of over 2000 m of Permo-Triassic in the Rathlin Trough, overlain by Jurassic and Cretaceous sediments in the south and south-east of this south-easterly tilted half-graben (Figure 27).

Triassic sediments occur at the north coast of Northern Ireland (Figure 28) on the shores of Lough Foyle and at Murlough Bay (Wilson, 1972). Elsewhere, the Triassic is overlain by Jurassic and Cretaceous sediments, and by extensive Tertiary basalts. Two boreholes on the coast of Northern Ireland (Figure 31) have penetrated Permian and Triassic sediments. The Magilligan borehole, north-east of Lough Foyle (Limavady 1:50 000 Solid Geology sheet 6), drilled 400 m of reddish brown sandstones and conglomerates of the Sherwood Sandstone Group overlain by 370 m of Mercia Mudstone Group comprising reddish brown anhydritic mudstones with partly pebbly sandstones. This is overlain by 22 m of grey mudstones of the Rhaetian Penarth Group, giving a total thickness of almost 800 m of Permo-Triassic rocks lying upon lower Namurian sandstones. The Port More borehole (Figure 31), drilled an almost 1200 m-thick sedimentary sequence lithologically similar to that in the Magilligan borehole. However, the Sherwood Sandstone Group here overlies a red sandstone sequence which contains rounded wind-

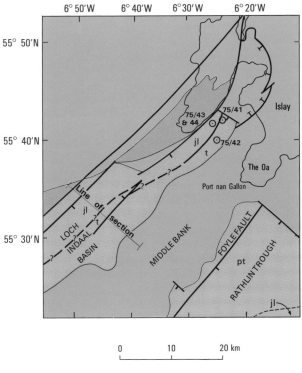

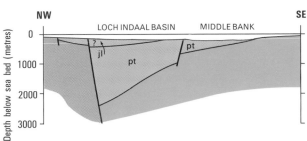

sandstones and conglomerates which are considered to be of Permo-Triassic age. Borehole 75/40 drilled 10 m of upward-fining, fine- to medium-grained, red sandstone with coarse-grained sandstone and conglomerate at the base of individual beds. Borehole 73/04 penetrated 3 m of fine-grained, purplish red sandstone passing upwards into conglomerate and conglomeratic sandstone. Borehole 73/28 drilled 2 m of coarse-grained, partly pebbly red sandstone that passes upwards into medium-grained, well-sorted sandstone with clasts or isolated beds of red mudstone.

On the west coast of Kintyre (Figure 28), two Permo-Triassic outliers occur beyond the eastern margin of the Rathlin Trough (Pringle, 1947). These outcrops comprise a sequence of fanglomerates and floodplain deposits, the former showing westerly current directions, indicating deposition from an upland area on the Scottish mainland to the east (Steel, 1977). In the Sound of Islay on the islet of Glas Eilean, there are interbedded alkali olivine-basalts and reddish brown sandstones that are partly conglomeratic. Although Pringle (1944) considered these to be Late Carboniferous in age, the lavas have been dated as Early Permian by Upton et al. (1987).

NORTH CHANNEL BASIN AND THE FIRTH OF CLYDE REGION

South-east of the Tow Valley Fault, the north-westerly trending North Channel Basin (Figure 28) contains over 1700 m of Permo-Triassic sediments (Deegan, 1978). Because of erosion by the strong, present-day bottom currents in the channel, Permo-Triassic rocks occur widely at sea bed, and many core samples of these redbeds have been collected (BGS Clyde Solid Geology sheet). The basin pass-

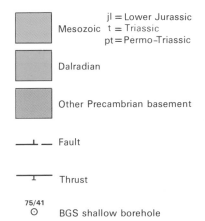

Figure 30 Map and section through the Loch Indaal Basin, south-west of Islay. See Figure 28 for location of area.

blown grains; this was tentatively ascribed to the Permian by Wilson (1972).

The Rathlin Trough extends north-eastwards into the Sound of Jura, and much of this basin has Permo-Triassic sediments at outcrop (Figure 28). Fine-grained red sandstone and calcareous mudstone interpreted as Permo-Triassic in age have been sampled at sea bed to the north-west of Rathlin Island (BGS Malin Solid Geology sheet). In the north-eastern part of the trough, three BGS boreholes (73/04, 73/28 and 75/40) have penetrated unfossiliferous, poorly indurated

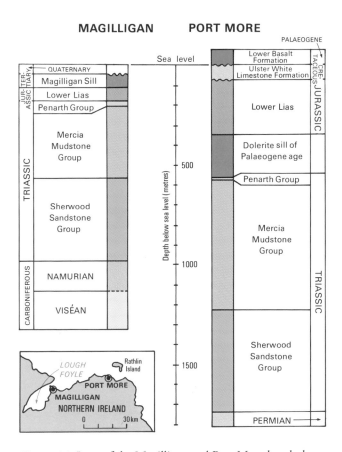

Figure 31 Logs of the Magilligan and Port More boreholes.

37

es north-eastwards into a number of small basins in the Firth of Clyde; these include the South-West Arran Trough, the North-East Arran Trough and the Carrick Basin (Figures 13 and 28). In this region, good onshore stratigraphical control in Arran means that Permian and Triassic sediments may be extrapolated offshore (BGS Clyde Solid Geology sheet), although they are all classified as Permo-Triassic on Figure 28.

Permo-Triassic rocks crop out on the east coast of Antrim only in the area to the south of Cushendall (Figure 28). Some 15 km south of the report area, the Larne No. 2 borehole (Penn et al., 1983) penetrated a much fuller Permo-Triassic succession which includes 600 m of Lower Permian tuffs and intermediate lavas overlain by 500 m of Permian sandstone, mudstone, dolomite and halite. Above lie 1800 m of Triassic Sherwood Sandstone Group and Mercia Mudstone Group sediments, the latter including 480 m of halite.

The succession in the South-West Arran Trough has been sampled by three BGS boreholes. Boreholes 71/01, 71/02 and 72/03 penetrated red sandstone and marl, with gypsum in bands up to 25 mm thick; a Triassic age is inferred from correlation with the onshore section of southern Arran. The presence of evaporites suggests the possibility of marine in-fluence in this area at some time during the Triassic. Indeed the Triassic halite deposits at Larne (Wilson, 1981; Penn et al., 1983) attest to the temporary proximity of the sea.

The Permo-Triassic of other parts of the Firth of Clyde region has been drilled in several BGS boreholes. Borehole 71/03, north of Arran, penetrated 18 m of massive, pebbly, red sandstone, conglomerate and thin red marl bands. In the Carrick Basin, boreholes 70/14 and 73/02 penetrated 4 m and 44 m respectively of red and purple, fine-grained, well-sorted, micaceous sandstone with siltstone partings and thin marl layers. Some thin bands of coarse-grained sandstone are also recorded. These lithologies correlate well with the Permian sandstones of Arran (Piper, 1970).

Immediately south of the Malin–Hebrides area, the north-north-westerly trending Stranraer Basin contains up to 1600 m of Permo-Triassic sediments (McLean and Deegan, 1978). In Ballantrae Bay, a small onshore outcrop of basal breccias, with clasts derived from the Ordovician Ballantrae Igneous Complex, underlies dune-bedded sandstone which has been assigned to the Permian (Greig, 1971). McLean and Wren (1978) demonstrated that this sequence represents the onshore part of a more widespread offshore Permo-Triassic cover.

7   Jurassic

Jurassic strata are widely distributed on land in the districts adjacent to the Malin–Hebrides sea area, and Jurassic rocks have been mapped in many offshore sedimentary basins (Figure 32). The thickest onshore sequence is found on Skye and Raasay, where around 450 m of limestones, mudstones and sandstones have been recorded. To the north and east, thin sequences are found on the Shiant Islands, at Gruinard Bay and at Applecross. Farther south, the Jurassic is exposed in Ardnamurchan, Mull, Eigg, Muck and Northern Ireland; the 200 m succession in Ardnamurchan and Mull was described by Hallam (1983) as a condensed sequence. The thickness of onshore Jurassic sequences contrasts considerably with those offshore, as the depositional basins initiated in the Late Palaeozoic continued to be active zones of accumulation. Up to 2500 m of Jurassic sediments may be preserved in the North Minch Basin (BGS Sutherland Solid Geology sheet).

At the end of the Triassic Period there was a lowering of global sea level (Figure 33), although tectonism in the UK area gave rise to a local transgression in Rhaetian times. The Jurassic is characterised by an overall eustatic rise in sea level (Haq et al., 1987); in Early Jurassic times this resulted in continued regional transgression and the inundation of much of north-western Europe. This transgressive phase is believed to have initiated a link between the Tethys and Arctic seas (Ziegler, 1981). The Late Triassic to Early Jurassic Rhaetian transgression moved northwards diachronously, and is recognised as having reached Mull in the Late Triassic, Ardnamurchan by the early Hettangian, and Skye in the late Hettangian (Oates, 1978; Morton et al., 1987; 1989). The start of the Middle Jurassic was marked by eustatic lowering of sea level synchronous with the onset of sea-floor spreading in the central Atlantic. Subsequently sea level began to rise, giving widespread transgression during the Late Jurassic.

In addition to these regional eustatic trends, local tectonic activity affected sedimentation, and is considered by Trueblood and Morton (1991) to have been the main control on Early and Middle Jurassic sedimentation west of the British Isles. Evidence for volcanism is abundant in the Middle Jurassic in the central North Sea, and there is evidence for Late Jurassic volcanism in Skye, which is inferred to be associated with rifting in the Rockall Trough (Knox, 1977).

The eustatic sea-level changes and tectonic activity combined to provide a variety of sedimentary conditions in northern Britain. In and around the north of Britain, Jurassic rocks are dominantly argillaceous or arenaceous, implying that nearby sediment source areas were being actively eroded during that time. Throughout the changes in sea level, the emergent Scottish Highlands and Shetland Platform appear to have provided a significant source of sediment. In the northern North Sea, Lower Jurassic (Statfjord Formation) sandstones contain abundant metamorphic rock fragments and fresh feldspar, indicating rapid erosion and deposition from a nearby uplifted orogenic belt (Hallam, 1983). Middle Jurassic (Rannoch Formation) sediments are rich in muscovite (Gray and Barnes, 1981), inferred by Hallam (1983) to have been derived from Moine schists of a Scottish Highland landmass. The Irish Massif, Rockall Bank, the Faeroe Plateau and the Hebrides Platform may also have been significant emergent features during the Jurassic (Ziegler, 1981).

During the Early and Late Jurassic transgressive phases, deposition was in dominantly shallow-marine environments. Middle Jurassic sediments are interpreted as shallow-marine or shoreface sands in the North Sea, but in the Inner Hebrides, the Great Estuarine Group is considered to have been deposited in shallow lagoons in which salinities varied from freshwater to marine, but were dominantly brackish (Hudson, 1963). A warm-temperate palaeoclimate during the Late Jurassic is suggested by the presence of reef corals in the marine sediments (Hallam, 1983).

NORTH LEWIS AND NORTH MINCH BASINS

The North Lewis Basin, which was a locus of significant sedimentation in the Permo-Triassic, continued to be a zone of deposition during the Jurassic. The basin is bounded to the east by the Minch Fault (Figure 32), and the Mesozoic sequence is thought to thicken to the north and west (BGS Lewis Solid Geology sheet). Some shallow-seismic records show a sequence of strong internal reflectors, interpreted as Permo-Triassic sandstones, overlain by an acoustically transparent sequence with a strong basal reflector. The upper sequence is interpreted as Jurassic. BGS borehole 77/08, drilled in the northern part of the North Lewis Basin, penetrated 8 m of very dark grey, silty mudstone that yielded an Early Jurassic sporomorph assemblage. The absence of the dinoflagellate cyst *Nannoceratopsis* may imply that the core is Lower Lias. The possible absence of younger Jurassic and Cretaceous strata from the basin and adjacent areas was believed by Hallam (1983) to be related more to pre-Tertiary uplift and erosion than to nondeposition, so their presence may yet be proven.

The North Minch Basin contains the thickest sequence of Jurassic in the report area, for the presence of around 2500 m of sediments is inferred from seismic-reflection surveys (BGS Sutherland Solid Geology sheet). The thickest sequence occurs immediately to the east of the Minch Fault, suggesting a degree of syndepositional movement, though there is no lithological evidence to support this contention. The Jurassic was deposited over Permo-Triassic sediments, and the entire Mesozoic sequence thins towards the east, where a Permo-Triassic outcrop fringes the basin. Onshore, between Gruinard Bay and Loch Ewe, there is a thin, faulted, coastal outcrop of Lower Jurassic overlying the Permo-Triassic. The outcrop comprises poorly exposed sandy limestone, argillaceous limestone and blue clay. The limestone is faulted against Torridonian sandstones to the south-east and is interpreted as not extending far offshore. Nearby loose blocks of limestone have yielded bivalves indicative of a Sinemurian age (Phemister, 1960).

Near the eastern limit of the Jurassic, borehole 72/33 penetrated 1.2 m of massive, black mudstone with pyrite fragments and Pliensbachian to Toarcian miospores. BGS borehole 85/08, some 30 km to the south and in a similar structural position, drilled 5 m of very dark grey to black, calcareous siltstone dated as early Sinemurian on the basis of miospore assemblages. The calcareous microfauna in the rock suggests a younger, but nonetheless Jurassic age.

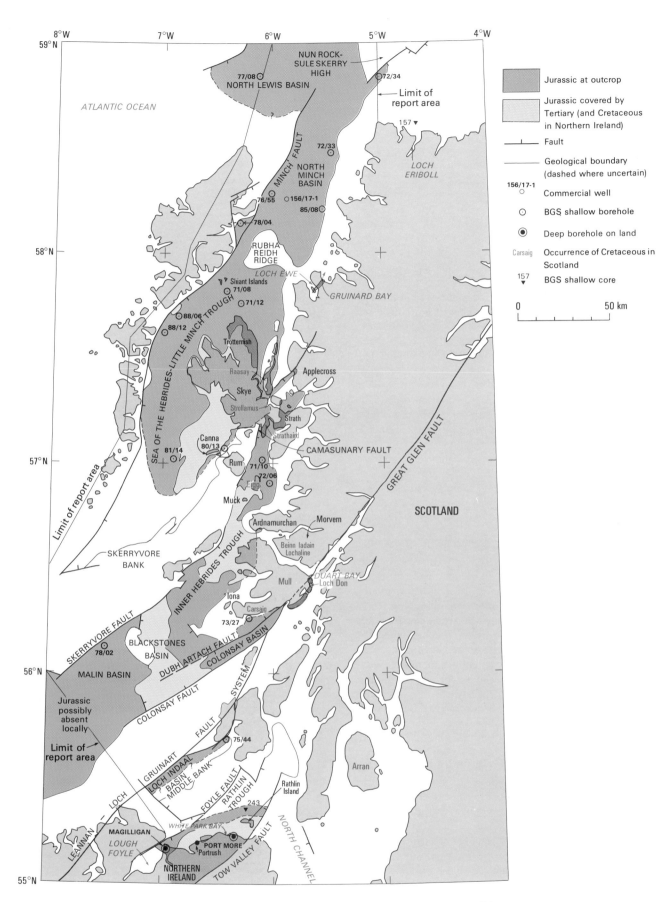

Figure 32 Distribution of Jurassic rocks, possibly including Cretaceous sediments in some offshore sequences. Occurrences of Cretaceous rocks in Scotland are also shown.

In the central part of the North Minch Basin, well 156/17-1 drilled 360 m of Lower Jurassic strata (Figure 29). The sequence is interpreted as comprising 56 m of Broadford Beds Formation overlain by 304 m of Pabba Shale Formation. The Broadford Beds Formation consists of medium-grained, well-cemented, hard to very hard, blocky, white sandstone interbedded with firm, homogeneous, pale grey mudstone. The top of the formation is a 1 m-thick band of hard, crystalline, white limestone. The Pabba Shale Formation comprises medium to dark grey mudstones which are moderately hard and blocky, and have a calcareous cement. In parts they are very calcareous and very micaceous, and include pods and lenses of fine- to very coarse-grained quartz sand.

Nearby BGS borehole 76/55 (Figure 32) penetrated 13 m of black mudstone and dark grey shales that yielded a late Hettangian to early Sinemurian microfauna. Near the east coast of Lewis, to the west of the Minch Fault, BGS borehole 78/04 penetrated 14 m of soft, black shale with ammonites which are not considered age diagnostic.

North of the Scottish mainland near the eastern boundary of the report area, BGS borehole 72/34 recovered 6.3 m of brick-red siltstone with pods and lenses of fine-grained sand. These sediments are bioturbated, and a tentative Early Jurassic age is inferred from a sparse palynomorph assemblage, which thereby provides further evidence of the late arrival of the Rhaetian transgression in northern parts.

The evidence from these boreholes suggests that, at least in the southern part of the North Minch Basin, the youngest rocks are of Early Jurassic age, and that there is a degree of uniformity of Lias facies throughout most of the North Minch Basin. It may be significant however that an isolated sample of hard, grey, Middle Jurassic limestone was drilled at the sea bed (Figure 32) a few kilometres north of Loch Eriboll within an area mapped as basement (BGS Sutherland Solid Geology sheet). Middle Jurassic rocks have also been drilled on the outer shelf to the north-west of Lewis (Stoker et al., in press).

In the extreme north of the report area, to the west of the Nun Rock–Sule Skerry High (Figure 32), sea-bed sampling has recovered a medium- to coarse-grained sandstone barren of fossils; this facies may be indicative of a Middle Jurassic age, or may be equivalent to the Broadford Beds Formation in well 156/17-1. The possible absence of Middle and Upper Jurassic sediments is attributed to erosion by Hallam (1983), though original nondeposition cannot be discounted.

SEA OF THE HEBRIDES–LITTLE MINCH TROUGH

South of the Rubha Reidh Ridge (Figure 32), the Sea of the Hebrides–Little Minch Trough contains some 1500 m of Jurassic sediments overlying rocks of Permo-Triassic age (Little Minch Solid Geology sheet). The Jurassic appears at outcrop on Skye and Raasay, where the stratigraphical coverage is almost complete (Hallam, 1983), with minor occurrences on the Shiant Islands (Penn and Merriman, 1978) and at Applecross (Searle, 1989).

Offshore, the Jurassic is bounded to the west by the Minch Fault, against which the thickest sequence of Jurassic is interpreted to occur. The eastern margin of the trough is taken as the basement ridge running south-south-west through Skye and Rum to the Skerryvore Bank. To the east of this ridge lies the Inner Hebrides Trough, which is considered to have been a separate depositional basin from the Sea of the Hebrides–Little Minch Trough, for although there is a similarity in the Lower and Upper Jurassic sequences (Morton, 1987), separate facies are recognised in the Middle Jurassic

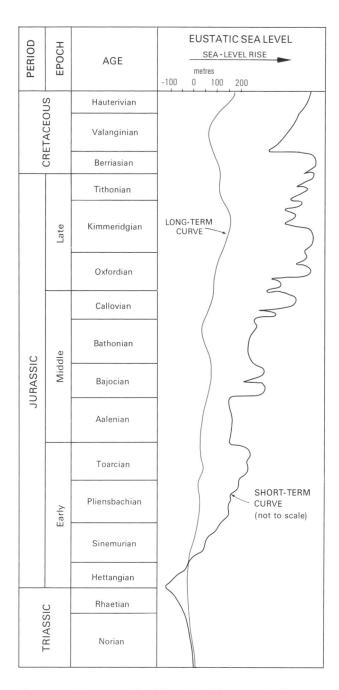

Figure 33 Eustatic sea level from Late Triassic to Early Cretaceous times. Composite short-term curve after Vail and Todd (1981) for the Triassic and Cretaceous, after Hallam (1978) for the Middle and Late Jurassic, and after Hallam (1981) for the Early Jurassic. Long-term curve after Haq et al. (1987).

(Morton, 1983). This suggests the basin separation was most significant during the Middle Jurassic, coincident with the relatively low rate of eustatic sea-level rise at that time (Figure 33).

The Jurassic of the Shiant Islands (Figure 32) consists of thermally metamorphosed shales up to 19 m thick (Walker, 1930). The presence of lower Toarcian ammonites (Penn and Merriman, 1978) suggests that these shales belong to the Portree Shale Formation.

At Applecross (Figure 32), 61 m of Lower Jurassic sediments rest on a well-developed Permo-Triassic calcrete, the presence of which indicates the development of a soil profile, and the possibility of a significant interval between the deposition of the Permo-Triassic and the Jurassic transgressive

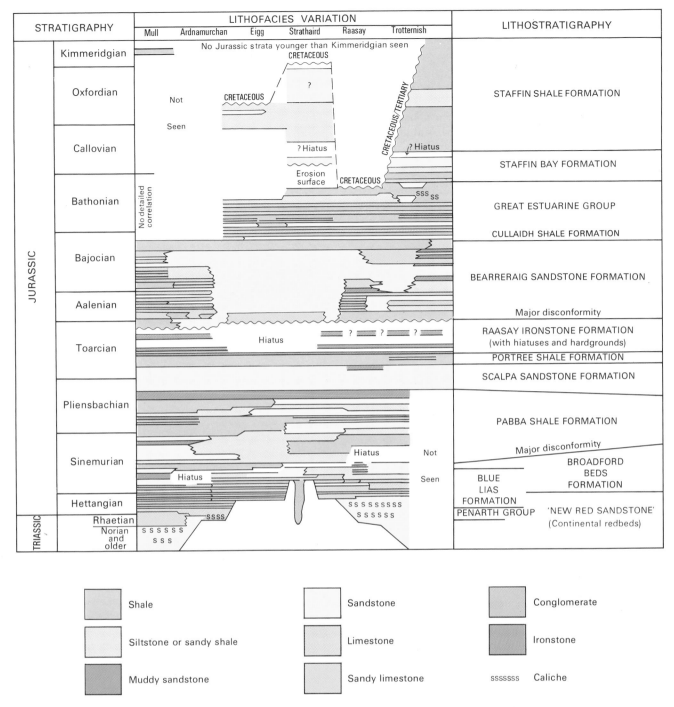

STRATIGRAPHY		LITHOFACIES VARIATION						LITHOSTRATIGRAPHY
		Mull	Ardnamurchan	Eigg	Strathaird	Raasay	Trotternish	
JURASSIC	Kimmeridgian	No Jurassic strata younger than Kimmeridgian seen						STAFFIN SHALE FORMATION
	Oxfordian	Not Seen	CRETACEOUS	CRETACEOUS	?			
	Callovian				? Hiatus	? Hiatus		STAFFIN BAY FORMATION
	Bathonian	No detailed correlation			Erosion surface	CRETACEOUS	sss ss	GREAT ESTUARINE GROUP / CULLAIDH SHALE FORMATION
	Bajocian							BEARRERAIG SANDSTONE FORMATION
	Aalenian							Major disconformity
	Toarcian			Hiatus	? ▬ ? ▬ ?			RAASAY IRONSTONE FORMATION (with hiatuses and hardgrounds) / PORTREE SHALE FORMATION / SCALPA SANDSTONE FORMATION
	Pliensbachian							PABBA SHALE FORMATION
	Sinemurian	Hiatus		Hiatus		Not Seen		Major disconformity / BROADFORD BEDS FORMATION
	Hettangian				ssssssss sssss			BLUE LIAS FORMATION
TRIASSIC	Rhaetian	ssss						PENARTH GROUP
	Norian and older	ssssss sss						'NEW RED SANDSTONE' (Continental redbeds)

Legend:
- Shale
- Siltstone or sandy shale
- Muddy sandstone
- Sandstone
- Limestone
- Sandy limestone
- Conglomerate
- Ironstone
- sssssss Caliche

Figure 34 Lateral variation in Upper Triassic to Jurassic lithofacies in the Inner Hebrides. After Morton et al. (1987) and Morton (1989).

phase. At the base, 8 m of interbedded mudstone, limestone and sandstone are overlain by 7 m of oolitic limestone (Searle, 1989). This is in turn overlain by 31 m of interbedded limestone and sandstone and the top 15 m of the section comprises an upward-coarsening siliciclastic sequence with limestone. The base of the Jurassic sequence, which is dated as late Hettangian, is interpreted as representing marine flooding of a subdued Triassic topography. This was followed by a range of depositional environments including shallow, carbonate shelf with patch reefs, oolitic shoal, restricted lagoon, beach and siliciclastic mudflats (Searle, 1989).

Skye and Raasay provide the thickest and most complete onshore Jurassic sections in the Malin–Hebrides area (Hallam, 1983). The terrestrial basal Jurassic is overlain by Sinemurian to Toarcian shallow-marine shales, siltstones, sandstones, ironstones and oolites which contain an almost complete succession of ammonite zones. Above these (Figure 34) lie coarse-grained, marine, clastic sediments of Aalenian

to Bajocian age, and the nonmarine Great Estuarine Group (Bajocian to Bathonian). Marine conditions were re-established during the Callovian.

On northern Skye, the base of the Jurassic in Trotternish is not exposed, and the oldest sediments are late Pliensbachian Scalpa Sandstone Formation sandstones and silty sandstones (Morton et al., 1987). These are overlain by the Portree Shale Formation, which represents deeper-water deposition, and the chamositic ironstone and mudstone of the Toarcian Raasay Ironstone Formation (Figure 34). Morton (1987) stated that the ironstone was laid down in a nonsubsiding, shallow-marine environment, though earlier work by Hallam (1981) had suggested that it may have been deposited in deep water that was starved of sediment. The Bearreraig Sandstone Formation, of Aalenian to Bajocian age, is evidence of further shallow-marine sedimentation at this time (Morton, 1987) and includes shales, impure limestones and sandstones. This is overlain by the largely Bathonian Great Estuarine Group, comprising shales, sandstones and limestones interpreted as lagoonal sediments. The higher Middle to Upper Jurassic (Callovian to Kimmeridgian) is represented by shallow-marine sediments of the Staffin Bay and Staffin Shale formations; these are dominantly shales, with thin limestones and sandstones, which are in places carbonaceous and become bituminous in the upper Oxfordian to Kimmeridgian.

On Raasay, Torridonian sandstones are overlain by basal Mesozoic sandstones of 'New Red Sandstone' facies. At their base, these sandstones are probably of Triassic age, but Morton (1987) suggested that the youngest beds are likely to be mid-Hettangian. The Broadford Beds Formation overlies the 'New Red Sandstone' facies sandstones; it comprises sandstones, mudstones and limestones whose thickest known onshore development is 140 m. The Pabba Shale Formation reaches a maximum thickness of 90 m in Raasay (Hallam 1983), and is overlain by the Portree Shale Formation and the Raasay Ironstone Formation. The dominantly shallow-marine sediments of the Lower Jurassic are unconformably overlain by the Bearreraig Sandstone Formation. This comprises shales, siltstones and sandstones with calcareous sandstones and sandy limestones in the upper part, and represents further shallow-marine sedimentation. As in Skye, this is overlain by the Great Estuarine Group, comprising shales, sandstones and limestones laid down in shallow lagoons of variable salinity (Morton, 1987). Upper Jurassic sediments are absent in Raasay, presumably removed by later erosion.

A number of BGS offshore boreholes in the Sea of the Hebrides–Little Minch Trough have drilled Jurassic strata. North of Trotternish, borehole 71/12 (Figure 32) penetrated 3.5 m of Lower Jurassic (?Middle Lias) grey sandstone that is calcareous throughout, with some mudstone pellets near the base. This is possibly a correlative of the Upper Broadford Beds Formation described by Morton (1987) at Hallaig, Raasay. Borehole 71/08, 8 km south-west of the Shiant Islands, penetrated 2.5 m of Upper Jurassic (probably Kimmeridgian), grey to black, silty shale which may be tentatively correlated with the Staffin Shale Formation on Skye. The stratigraphical range of these occurrences demonstrates a complexity of distribution which cannot be readily unravelled.

West of the northern tip of Skye, BGS borehole 88/06 (Figure 32) drilled 7 m of very dark grey to black, calcareous mudstone which yielded a Middle Jurassic fauna and microflora. The fossils include a specimen of the upper Bajocian ammonite *Garantiana garantiana* (d'Orbigny), probably from the Dichotoma Subzone. The lithology of the core from which this specimen was recovered is similar in many respects to the upper Bajocian Garantiana Clay Member of the Bearreraig Sandstone Formation. Above this fossiliferous horizon, the mudstone yielded the upper Bajocian to lower Bathonian dinoflagellate cyst *Carpathodinium predae* (Beju) Drugg, which suggests that it may be part of the Cullaidh Shale Formation at the base of the Great Estuarine Group (Figure 34).

Farther south, borehole 80/13, north-east of the island of Canna (Figure 32), penetrated 29 m of Jurassic calcarenite, biosparite and microsparite. Shelly material is concentrated in thin bands of whole and broken bivalves, including *Gryphaea,* and belemnites occur throughout the unit. At the base of the core, the rock is a brecciated sandy limestone with a band of pebbles, apparently of Torridonian affinity. Calcareous foraminifera indicate that this core is Liassic; the presence of *Citherina* cf *clathrata* (Terquem), *C. colliezi* (Terquem), and *Palmula deslongchampsi* (Terquem) suggest an age older than Toarcian.

BGS borehole 81/14, 15 km west-south-west of Canna, drilled 3.9 m of calcareous siltstone and mudstone with bands of limestone, overlying dark grey, bituminous mudstone. The sediments yielded abundant bivalves, both isolated and as death assemblages in thin bands. The miospore assemblage includes well-preserved specimens of *Callialasporites dampieri* (Balme) Sukh Dev that indicate a probable Middle Jurassic age for this core. The co-occurrence of *Parvisaccites enigmatus* Couper and *Lycopodiacidites spinatus* Pocock indicates a Bathonian age, as does the ostracod *Darwinula incurva* Bate, which is associated with low-salinity conditions. This, together with a freshwater/brackish microplankton assemblage, suggests that these sediments are part of the Great Estuarine Group.

INNER HEBRIDES TROUGH

The outcrop of Jurassic rocks in the Inner Hebrides Trough is divided by a wide tract of Tertiary basalts extending north-westwards from Mull (Figure 32). The northern part of the outcrop stretches southwards from Skye to Ardnamurchan, whereas the southern part lies to the west and south of Mull.

On Strath and the Strathaird peninsula, the Lower Broadford Beds are less sandy than on Raasay to the north, and limestone is more dominant. The sequence is similar to the Blue Lias of southern England both lithologically and palaeontologically (Oates, 1978). The Broadford Beds Formation is succeeded disconformably by the Pabba Shale Formation, which passes up into the Pliensbachian to Toarcian Scalpa Sandstone Formation. These formations, together with the Portree Shale Formation, suggest dominantly shallow-marine environments of deposition during the Early Jurassic. Morton's (1987) interpretation of the environment of deposition of the succeeding Raasay Ironstone Formation suggests that the hiatuses and hardgrounds represent a brief regressive phase that coincides with a eustatic lowering of sea level identified by Hallam (1981). To the south, in Ardnamurchan, Morvern and Mull, these formations are all represented by attenuated sequences.

Onshore, the Lias of the Inner Hebrides Trough is overlain everywhere by the Bearreraig Sandstone Formation and the Great Estuarine Group, although the sequence is thinner in the south. The sandstones of the Bearreraig Sandstone Formation are characterised by a cross-bedded facies in Strathaird and Ardnamurchan (Morton, 1983), and although this facies is present on Raasay, it is otherwise absent from the Sea of the Hebrides–Little Minch Trough, where massive sandstones and siltstones represent a deeper-water environment of deposition. The Great Estuarine Group in Strathaird is overlain by a sequence of Upper Jurassic sandstones and siltstones representing further shallow-marine and tidal sedimentation (Figure 34). Upper Jurassic sediments are not generally preserved in the south, though Kimmeridgian shales are present at Duart Bay in Mull.

Two BGS boreholes have penetrated Jurassic strata in the Inner Hebrides Trough (Figure 32). East of Rum, borehole 71/10 penetrated 2 m of fine-grained, grey, muddy, sandy and sporadically shelly limestone that is partly micritic and bioturbated. This limestone contains a number of microfossils which are not diagnostic but, when considered with the lithology, suggest correlation with the Scalpa Sandstone Formation. In this vicinity, the diachronous Scalpa Sandstone Formation is Pliensbachian in age. To the east of Eigg, borehole 72/06 drilled 1 m of fine-grained, massive, calcareous sandstone with thin, black, organic-rich partings. The lithology is similar to that in 71/10, but the core is devoid of palynomorphs; the organic-rich partings yielding only carbonised plant tissue. To the south of the Mull basalts, a sea-bed rock-drill sample 6 km west of Iona (Figure 32) recovered silt-grade calcarenite which, although unfossiliferous, has been interpreted as Jurassic.

It is not possible to determine intra-Mesozoic stratigraphical boundaries in the offshore areas of the Inner Hebrides Trough. The sparse samples suggest that although Jurassic strata may occur over much of the basin, they may be thinner or absent in the south. South of Mull, BGS borehole 73/27 penetrated rocks of Permo-Triassic facies.

COLONSAY AND MALIN BASINS

The Colonsay and Malin basins have no onshore outcrop, although Lower Jurassic rocks occur on the south coast of Mull (Figure 32). South of the Inner Hebrides Trough, between the Dubh Artach and Colonsay faults, the Colonsay Basin comprises a graben of Mesozoic sediments overlain in the south-west by Tertiary rocks. Sea-bed sampling in the northern part of the basin has recovered silicified sandy limestone, and 6 km north-west of Colonsay, a well-bedded calcareous sandstone has been assigned to the Middle Jurassic (BGS Tiree Solid Geology sheet).

The Malin Basin is bounded to the north-west by the Skerryvore Fault and to the south-east by the Colonsay Fault, although in the south the latter fault is overlain by Mesozoic sediments. To the east, the boundary of the basin is marked by the Blackstones Bank igneous centre (Figure 4); samples of undated calcareous metasediments recovered from the centre (Durant et al., 1982) are perhaps most likely to be of Jurassic age. In the west of the Malin Basin, the sediments are intruded by numerous sills and dykes of Tertiary age which interrupt well-spaced, dipping, seismic reflectors within sediments interpreted as Mesozoic in age (Evans et al., 1980). These reflectors suggest a series of north-easterly trending fold axes which are parallel to the faulted margins of the basin (Dobson and Whittington, 1992).

BGS borehole 78/02, in the northern part of the Malin Basin, penetrated 5.8 m of hard, dark grey siltstone that is calcareous and carbonaceous in part, with fossils including ammonite fragments and plant-stem impressions. Palynomorphs suggest that the sediments are of Early to Middle Jurassic age; the presence of the dinoflagellate cyst *Nannoceratopsis senex* van Helden indicates a probable Toarcian age. In both the Colonsay and Malin basins, it is likely that the Jurassic cover is thin, and may be absent in the south-east where the Permo-Triassic may crop out.

LOCH INDAAL BASIN AND RATHLIN TROUGH

The Loch Indaal Basin is a north-westerly dipping half-graben that lies south-east of the Leannan–Loch Gruinart fault system. In the north-eastern part of the basin, fold axes are seen to trend north-east to south-west along the axis of the basin, and there is good borehole control on the succes-

sion. Two boreholes sampled the Triassic (Figure 30), one penetrating the Rhaetian, and farther north-west borehole 75/44 penetrated 15.15 m of a very dark grey, slightly silty mudstone that is micaceous in parts and includes scattered bivalves and ammonites (Figure 32). The mudstone is highly calcareous at the base where there is a thin (5 cm) limestone band, and becomes less calcareous upwards. Ammonite fragments suggest that the beds are within the Obtusum Zone of the upper Sinemurian. A diverse bivalve assemblage provides little evidence, though a specimen of *?Laevitrigonia troedssoni* Melville, which farther south is usually associated with the lower Pliensbachian, is present. Dinoflagellate-cyst evidence suggests a Sinemurian age, largely due to the presence of *Liasidum variabile* Drugg without associated *Nannoceratopsis*. The Triassic–Jurassic boundary has been tentatively extended south-westwards (Figure 32), and it is conjectured that post-depositional movement on the Loch Gruinart fault system has preserved the Lower Jurassic sediments adjacent to the faulted half-graben margin.

To the south-east of the Middle Bank, Jurassic sediments in the south-easterly tilted Rathlin Trough are largely overlain by Upper Cretaceous Chalk and Tertiary lavas. In the offshore part of the Rathlin Trough, as on land, most of the outcrop is probably of Permo-Triassic age, with a fringe of Jurassic (Figure 32). The Magilligan borehole (Figure 31), east of Lough Foyle, penetrated 90 m of Lower Jurassic sediments beneath a massive sill. These sediments, in which the Hettangian Planorbis Zone has been recognised (Wilson, 1981), and others exposed nearby which range up to the Semicostatum Zone of the lower Sinemurian, comprise grey mudstones, siltstones and thin limestone stringers. The latter become more common in the upper part of the section.

To the east, the Lower Jurassic crops out near Portrush and at White Park Bay (Wilson and Manning, 1978), where it comprises grey mudstones and shales of late Sinemurian to early Pliensbachian age. The Port More borehole (Figure 31) penetrated almost 250 m of Lower Jurassic mudstone of early Sinemurian to early Pliensbachian age, ranging from the Semicostatum Zone to the Ibex Zone (Wilson, 1981). A sea-bed sample 5 km north of Rathlin Island recovered very dark grey, very micaceous, silty mudstone with a palynomorph assemblage suggesting a Sinemurian age.

East of the Tow Valley Fault, there is no evidence of Jurassic strata overlying the Permo-Triassic sediments offshore. Jurassic sediments were possibly not deposited here, but have more probably been stripped off by later erosion, for clasts of middle and upper Lias sediments occur in the basal conglomerate of the Cretaceous in north Antrim (Wilson, 1972). Over 50 m of early Liassic marine sediments were drilled in the Larne No. 1 borehole immediately south of the report area (Wilson, 1972). These rocks, predominantly dark grey mudstones of the Planorbis to Angulata zones (Wilson, 1981), overlie Penarth Group shale, mudstone and siltstones (Manning and Wilson, 1975).

8 Cretaceous

The global sea-level changes which were a major control on Jurassic depositional patterns continued to influence sedimentation during the Cretaceous, although local tectonics again played a significant role (Fyfe et al., 1981). Vail and Todd (1981) demonstrated a sea-level drop at the end of the Berriasian (Figure 33) before a steady eustatic rise from the early Valanginian to the Aptian, followed by a further lowering during the Aptian to Albian. From Albian to early Maastrichtian times, sea level rose to around 250 m above the present level (Haq et al., 1987). The subsequent rapid eustatic fall in the late Maastrichtian may have been related to progressive subcontinental plate consumption (Hallam, 1984).

Cretaceous strata are very poorly represented in the Malin–Hebrides area, but this may well be the result of pre-Tertiary erosion rather than nondeposition. The extent of such erosion is emphasised by Hallam (1983), who interpreted the thin Cretaceous sediments as isolated remnants of more extensive marine deposits. There is limited onshore outcrop of Cretaceous rocks on Mull and Morvern (Figure 32), where sequences up to 20 m thick are found. These comprise glauconitic sandstone overlain by 'white' sandstones and several centimetres of clay, all of Cenomanian age, and a thin cover of silicified, white, Santonian chalk. Upper Cretaceous sediments are also identified in Skye, Raasay, Eigg, and in the Central Vent on Arran, but are best developed in Northern Ireland, where they are widely preserved beneath Tertiary basalts.

Wilson (1972) divided the Upper Cretaceous of Northern Ireland into a lower arenaceous sequence, the Hibernian Greensands Formation, and an upper calcareous sequence, the Ulster White Limestone Formation (Figure 35). The Hibernian Greensands Formation represents sedimentation from Cenomanian to mid-Santonian times, and includes two intervals of nondeposition. Wilson (1972) proposed that the deposition of these sediments extended in a swath from the Irish Sea northwards through the North Channel to Mull (Figure 36a). Deposition of the overlying Chalk (Fletcher, 1977) was more extensive (Figure 36b) as a result of eustatic sea-level rise, during which upstanding massifs such as the Highland Border Ridge were progressively inundated (Wilson, 1972). The base of the formation is therefore diachronous (Figure 35). Deposition continued from mid-Santonian to Maastrichtian times, although with one or more nonsequences. The Ulster White Limestone Formation is similar to the Upper Chalk of England and probably shared the same environment of deposition, but has been subjected to diagenetic recrystallisation, making it much harder than its southern correlative (Fletcher, 1977).

Cretaceous sediments crop out along the northern coast of Northern Ireland west of Castlerock, at Portrush and at White Park Bay (Figure 37). Near Castlerock, the Cretaceous comprises mainly the Ulster White Limestone Formation, which at outcrop nearby includes glauconitic and stromatolitic limestones, suggesting that this area was near the basin margin (Wilson, 1972; 1981). The narrow outcrop between the Lias and the overlying Antrim plateau basalts becomes more extensive offshore (BGS Malin Solid Geology sheet), where BGS borehole 75/39 (Figure 37) penetrated 2.5 m of chalk with flints, tentatively dated as Santonian. This borehole is the only definitive offshore occurrence of Cretaceous

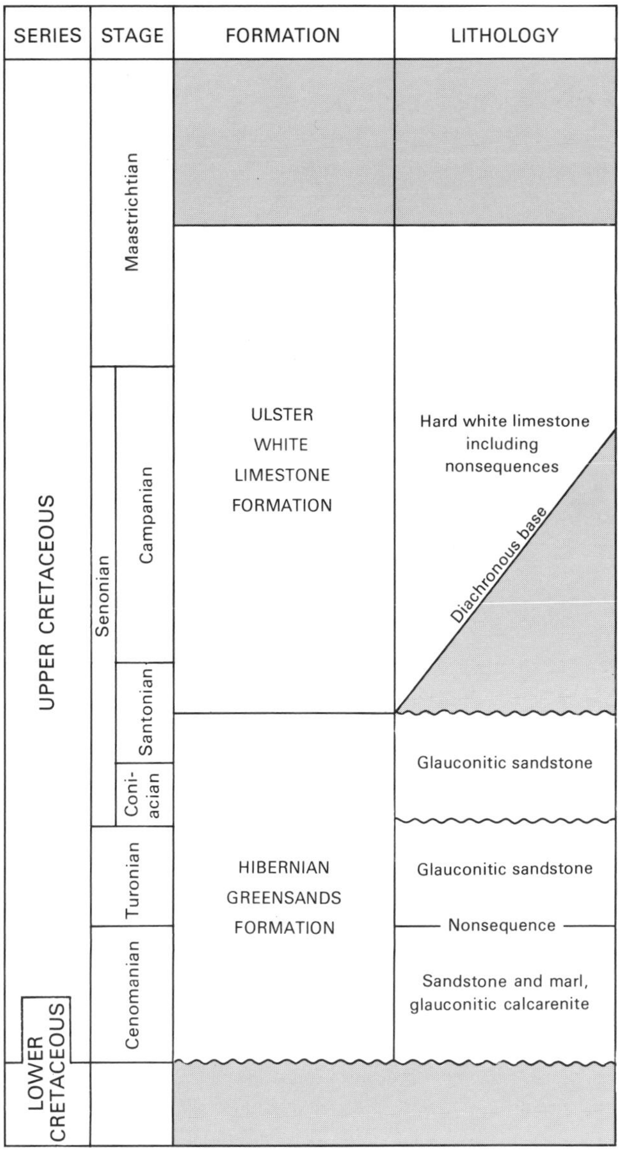

SERIES	STAGE	FORMATION	LITHOLOGY
UPPER CRETACEOUS	Maastrichtian		
	Senonian — Campanian	ULSTER WHITE LIMESTONE FORMATION	Hard white limestone including nonsequences / Diachronous base
	Santonian		
	Coniacian	HIBERNIAN GREENSANDS FORMATION	Glauconitic sandstone
	Turonian		Glauconitic sandstone / Nonsequence
	Cenomanian		Sandstone and marl, glauconitic calcarenite
LOWER CRETACEOUS			

Figure 35 Twofold division of Cretaceous sediments in Northern Ireland. After Wilson (1972).

in the Malin–Hebrides sea area. At Portrush, the onshore outcrop of Chalk is interpreted as extending up to a kilometre offshore. East of White Park Bay, in the Port More borehole (Figure 31), 90 m of the Ulster White Limestone Formation provide a comprehensive Upper Cretaceous stratigraphical sequence (Wilson and Manning, 1978), although correlation with the Upper Cretaceous of southern England has been hampered by the lack of zonal ammonites in the Northern Ireland sequence (Wilson, 1981).

East of the Tow Valley Fault, there is no evidence of either Jurassic or Cretaceous strata occurring offshore, although Upper Cretaceous remnants are preserved beneath Tertiary basalts on the Highland Border Ridge (Figure 37), and a block of chalk has been recovered from a Tertiary vent in Arran (Gunn, 1903). However, to the north-west of Ireland, on the edge of the Donegal Basin, well 12/13-1A penetrated

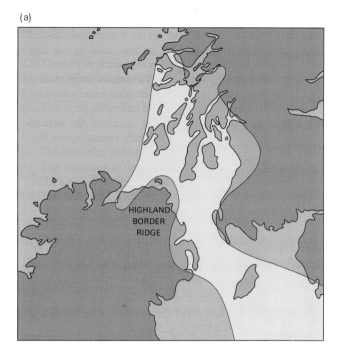

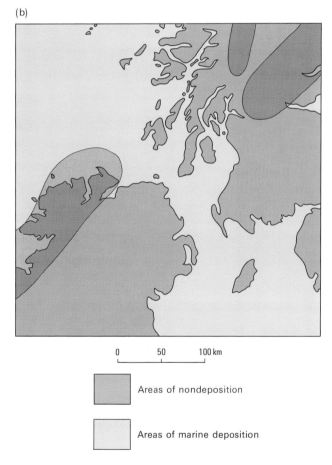

HIGHLAND
BORDER
RIDGE

0   50   100 km

Areas of nondeposition

Areas of marine deposition

Figure 36 Late Cretaceous palaeogeographic reconstructions. (a) Cenomanian (Hibernian Greensands Formation). (b) Late Santonian (Ulster White Limestone Formation). After Wilson (1972).

1200 m of Cretaceous to Tertiary sediments (Tate and Dobson, 1989) overlying around 100 m of Hettangian to Sinemurian dolomite and argillaceous limestone. This occurrence serves to support the proposition of extensive deposition of Cretaceous sediments in the southern part of the Malin–Hebrides area.

No Cretaceous sediments have been sampled farther north in the report area, and a sequence of very limited thickness would not be expected to have any significant expression on seismic records. Thin Cretaceous sediments may be preserved in some Mesozoic basins, as indicated from the surrounding land geology (Hallam, 1983), where Cretaceous greensand and chalk is preserved locally.

On Skye, at Strathaird and Strollamus (Figure 32), outcrops of Cretaceous sediments comprise sequences 2 m and 5 m in thickness respectively. At Strathaird, calcareous grit is overlain by a sandy limestone, whereas at Strollamus, calcareous grit underlies white limestone which has yielded the Late Cretaceous bivalve *Inoceramus* (Bell and Harris, 1986).

Minor outcrops of Upper Cretaceous strata beneath Tertiary lavas on Eigg, Mull and in Morvern indicate that the Cretaceous may occur in the Inner Hebrides Trough. At Loch Don (Richey, 1961), around 3 m of greensand has been dated as Cenomanian by the presence of the ammonite *Schloenbachia intermedia* (Mantell). Within the Cretaceous greensand at Lochaline, there occurs 12 m of white sandstone; this is almost pure silica rock that has been worked for glass sand (Hallam, 1983). The maximum thickness of Cretaceous in western Scotland is found on Beinn Iadain in Morvern, where 20 m of Cenomanian greensand is overlain by 0.5 m of silicified chalk.

46

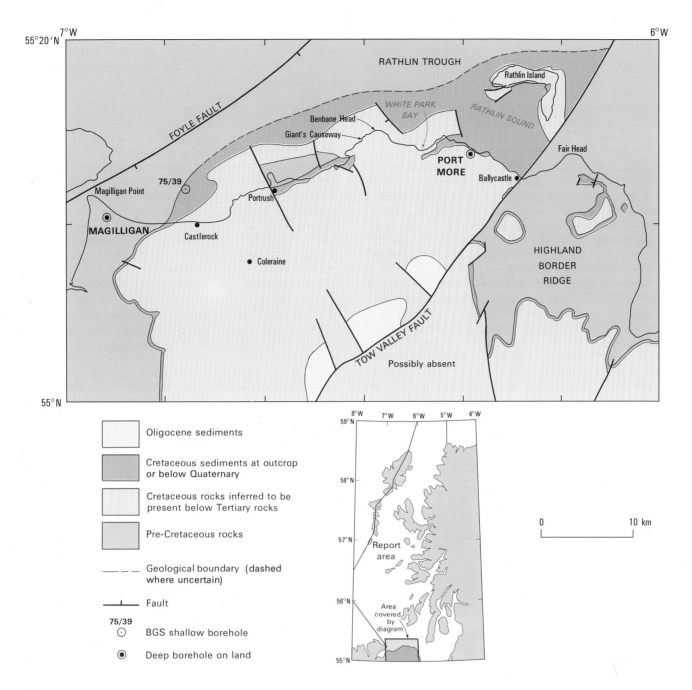

Figure 37 Distribution of Cretaceous rocks in and around the Rathlin Trough. The distribution of Oligocene sediments is also shown.

9 Tertiary

The North American continent had begun to separate from the European and Greenland plate in Jurassic time, but during the late Paleocene to early Eocene, a spreading centre developed between Greenland and north-west Europe; this led to the formation of the north-east Atlantic (Upton, 1988). The new tectonic regime in the north-east Atlantic region resulted in extensive volcanicity on both the Greenland and European/Rockall continental margins, including the Faeroes, western Britain and Ireland. In the British Isles, this volcanicity generally predated, or was contemporaneous with, continental separation (Knox and Morton, 1988; Boulter and Kvacek, 1989). Evidence of this early Tertiary volcanic interval is found both onshore and offshore, concentrated around western Scotland and Northern Ireland, but extending as far south as Lundy in the Bristol Channel.

The land around the report area has long been well known for its Tertiary igneous centres and extensive basalt lavas, particularly on Skye, Arran, Mull and Rum, and at Ardnamurchan and Northern Ireland (Sutherland, 1982). Figure 3 shows the broadly north-south alignment of the British Tertiary Volcanic Province (BTVP) centres in the area. Sills and extensive dyke swarms are even more widespread, and extend into England and Wales. Recent work on the continental shelf around Scotland has identified more igneous centres, including the Erlend centre north of Shetland (Gatliff et al., 1984), the Geikie and Darwin centres west of the Hebrides (Evans et al., 1989; Abraham and Ritchie, 1991), and the Blackstones Bank centre within the report area (McQuillin et al., 1975; Durant et al., 1976). The Blackstones Bank igneous centre is located some 35 km south-south-west of Tiree (Figures 2 and 3), and with a length of outcrop of over 20 km, is larger than the Tertiary centres found on the adjacent land.

Basalt lavas extend offshore from the known land outcrops, and other major occurrences of lavas have been located farther west and north-west on the outer Hebridean shelf (Stoker et al., 1988) and in the Rockall Trough. The latter had not subsided to its present form at the time of the volcanic activity (Wood et al., 1988; Morton et al., 1988). This volcanicity close to the continental margin is in marked contrast to the contemporaneous marine-clastic sedimentation which prevailed in south-eastern England and the North Sea, although ashes derived from the volcanic areas occur in the upper Paleocene and lower Eocene sediments of the North Sea Basin (Knox and Morton, 1983; 1988).

Dating of the volcanic episode has been the subject of controversy (Upton, 1988), but it appears to have spanned the interval from 63 to 52 Ma, with activity reaching a peak around 59 Ma, towards the end of the Paleocene (Musset et al., 1988). During the Eocene, the north-west British Isles were subjected to erosion in a humid, subtropical climate (Wilkinson et al., 1980). No sediments of this age have been located on the inner Scottish shelf or the adjacent land, although great thicknesses of sediment were being deposited on the outer Hebridean shelf and in the Rockall Trough, which had begun to subside (Wood et al., 1987). Much of this sediment is likely to have been derived from rapid erosion of the Hebridean volcanic terrain (Emeleus, 1985; Hall, 1991).

Oligocene nonmarine sediments were deposited in many regions of western Britain. These are now preserved on land in basins as far apart as Bovey Tracey, Dutson and Petrockstow

in Devon in the south, to the rather larger Lough Neagh Basin of Northern Ireland in the north (Curry et al., 1978). More Oligocene deposits (Figure 37) have been described recently from small basins along the Tow Valley Fault in Antrim (Griffith et al., 1987). Oligocene basins have also been identified offshore in the Stanley Bank Basin north-west of Devon (Davies, 1987; Fletcher, 1975), and off Mochras in the Tremadog Bay Basin (Dobson and Whittington, 1987). Within the report area (Figure 3), Oligocene sediments are present in the Canna Basin (Smythe and Kenolty, 1975; Evans et al., 1979b), the Blackstones Basin (Smythe and Kenolty, 1975; BGS Tiree Solid Geology sheet) and in the Little Minch (Evans et al., 1991). These sediments have been preserved in downfaulted or downwarped basins that formed during a period of general emergence of the Scottish Massif; Muir Wood (1989) has suggested that the basins lie along a late Oligocene subplate boundary.

During the Oligocene, deposition continued, albeit intermittently (Jones et al., 1986), in what had become deep water in the Rockall Trough to the west. Sedimentation on the outermost shelf slowly encroached on to the continental shelf during the Miocene, although deposits of that age are now found only on the outer shelf. No Neogene sediments are known to exist in the report area or on the adjacent land, and George (1967) deduced that the landscape of Northern Ireland and other parts of upland Britain were formed during the late Tertiary. Watson (1977) has estimated a very low rate of erosion for the Outer Hebrides, and suggested that the summits of the mountains of Harris are still at almost the same level as was the early Tertiary land surface. Hall (1991) also argued that despite deep weathering, surface levels in Scotland did not change significantly during the Neogene.

LOWER TERTIARY VOLCANIC ROCKS

Many of the districts surrounding the report area have become classical areas in British geology for the study of volcanic rocks (Richey, 1961; Upton, 1988). Offshore, basalt plateau lavas have been mapped, as have numerous minor intrusions, and a major intrusive igneous centre at Blackstones Bank.

Plateau lavas

The plateau lavas are predominantly basaltic, and were erupted subaerially on to a landscape of low relief. Individual flows are commonly separated by thin fossil soils, for oxidised, reddened tops of the flows were produced by deep weathering during intervals of volcanic quiescence. Thin interbasaltic sedimentary beds also occur, as well as ashy and tuffaceous bands which resulted from explosive activity during eruption. In the Scottish area, alkali basalts were later accompanied by hawaiites and other related differentiated lavas. Tholeiitic flows occur in the uppermost parts of some Scottish sequences (Emeleus, 1983), and are dominant in the middle part of the Antrim sequence (Wilson, 1972).

The lavas were generally extruded early in the cycle of igneous activity, although eruption locally continued throughout; the Canna Lava Formation of Canna and northern Rum postdates the intrusion of the central igneous complex

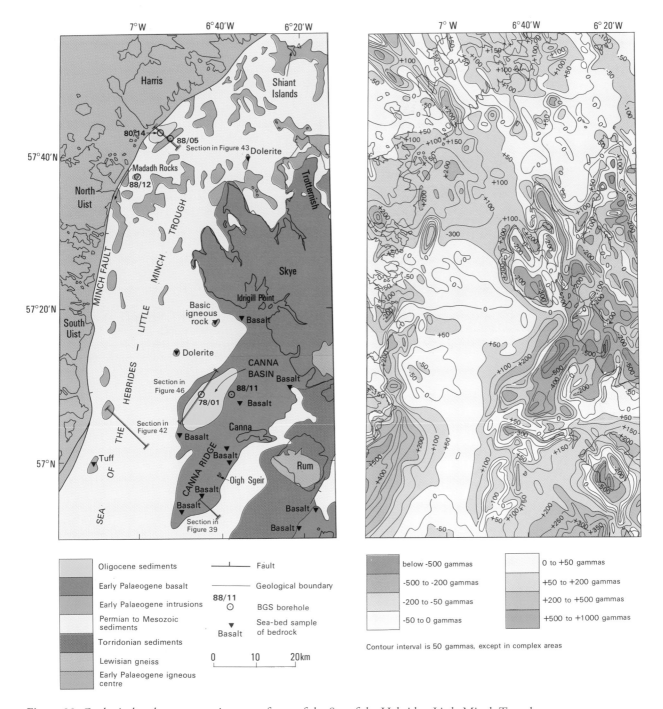

Figure 38 Geological and aeromagnetic maps of part of the Sea of the Hebrides–Little Minch Trough.

(Mussett et al., 1988). Emeleus (1983) summarised evidence to indicate that many Scottish lavas were erupted from fissure systems or small vents, as was wholly the case in Ireland (Preston, 1981). Tholeiitic lavas however tend to have a geographical association with the intrusive complexes, from which their magmas may have been derived.

Tertiary lavas have been identified offshore in three main regions of the report area: Skye–Canna, Mull, and Antrim (Figure 3; Curry et al., 1978). The distribution of the basalts is clearly illustrated by the pattern of magnetic anomalies (Figure 6; BGS Aeromagnetic Anomaly sheets). The high-frequency, largely negative anomalies associated with the basalts contrast with the more subdued anomalies of adjacent sedimentary strata (Figure 38). However, the contrast is not so clear when the basalts overlie, or are adjacent to, basement rocks. The limit of the lavas is commonly, but by no means ubiquitously, a prominent submarine escarpment associated

with a topographic change from the rather flat but undulating, outcropping lavas to lower-lying, softer and eroded Mesozoic rocks which are generally covered by thick glacial deposits (Figure 39). Bathymetry therefore tends to be important in delimiting the extent of the lavas. Internal layering seen in the lava pile onshore is not normally reflected on seismic records since the seismic energy generally fails to penetrate their strongly reflecting top, but some poorly defined dipping reflectors can be observed (Figure 39).

THE SKYE–CANNA REGION

Much of the Isle of Skye is covered by basalt flows which form high cliffs in the west and north-west of the island, and produce a spectacular escarpment with landslipping (Ballantyne et al., 1991) along the eastern part of the Trotternish Peninsula (see Front Cover). In the north, these flows extend offshore little farther than the coastline (Figure

49

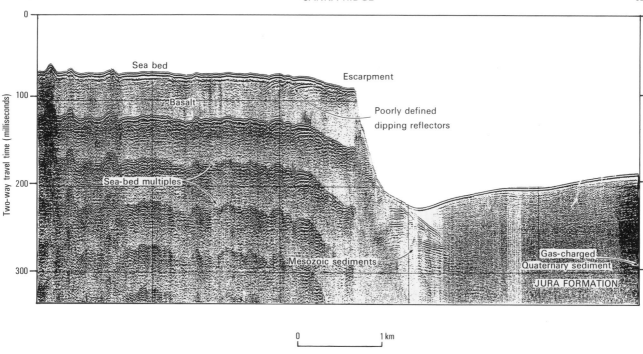

Figure 39 Annotated sparker profile across the basalt-plateau scarp south-west of Canna. For location see Figure 38.

38), but to the south-west they continue offshore to Canna, Oigh Sgeir and beyond, forming the Canna Ridge (BGS Little Minch Solid Geology sheet). The offshore coverage of basalts to the south-west of Skye is some 700 sq km in area, equivalent to that exposed on Mull (Emeleus, 1983), and is clearly outlined by aeromagnetic anomalies (Figure 38).

The limit of the basalts in this region can normally be identified from the bathymetry (Figures 2, 3 and 39). Eden et al. (1971), using observations from a submersible, described the plateau edge at two locations south-west and west of Canna, where it forms a series of vertical faces and ledges above a scree slope with an overall slope of 45°. Samples of ophitic olivine-basalt have been obtained at the sea bed both off Idrigill Point, Skye (Binns et al., 1974b) and south-west of Canna. BGS borehole 88/11 to the north of Canna (Figure 38) recovered fractured, altered, amygdaloidal basalt in which two individual flows were recognised. The scoriaceous top of the lower flow, and reddening elsewhere in the core, indicate that the basalt was extruded subaerially. The thickness of the offshore Skye–Canna basalt succession is estimated from gravity and seismic evidence to be up to 1000 m (Smythe and Kenolty, 1975); this compares with some 600 m of basalt onshore on Skye and Canna (Anderson and Dunham, 1966; Richey, 1961). The overall geometry of the basalts is not known, although it has been deduced that the Oligocene sediments of the Canna Basin (Figure 12) occur in a downwarped section of the basalts (Smythe and Kenolty, 1975; Stein, 1988).

THE MULL REGION

The extensive basalt lavas on Mull are now 1800 m thick, the maximum preserved thickness established in the BTVP (Emeleus, 1983). They extend eastwards to Morvern and north to Ardnamurchan, although it is considered unlikely that a connection exists across the Sound of Mull (BGS Argyll and Tiree Solid Geology sheets). The main offshore area of basalts lies to the west and north-west, where 630 sq km of basalt (Emeleus, 1983) extend almost as far as Coll, to include Muck and form most of Eigg (Figure 40). The extent of the

basalt can be identified from aeromagnetic anomalies (BGS Tiree Aeromagnetic Anomaly sheet), although the limits are not as clearly defined as in the region south-west of Skye.

Several samples of basalt, including amygdaloidal basalt, have been recovered from the central and southern parts of the outcrop; one sample between Coll and Muck was located close to a *Pisces* submersible traverse (C–D in Figure 40) described by Eden et al. (1971), who considered the rock there to be Torridonian due to its observed similarity to strata a few kilometres to the north-west on traverse A–B. However their echosounder traces (reproduced in Figure 40) clearly differentiate the relatively flat-topped basalt from the more rounded Torridonian topography. A sample recovered 2.8 km south-east of Eigg is a coarsely ophitic olivine-basalt (Binns et al., 1974b).

The southern boundary of the basalts around Staffa and the Treshnish Islands is a very strongly defined bathymetric scarp up to 100 m in height (Figures 2 and 40), although the scarp is not present at the extreme west of the outcrop. To the west, the basalts abut Lewisian rocks along the Skerryvore Fault (Figure 40), indicating that vertical movement on the fault here continued at least into Eocene times. To the north of Coll, the basalts appear to overlie Torridonian sediments, and a sinuous boundary has been drawn where the relatively flat-topped basalts contrast with the more irregular topography of the Precambrian sandstones. The eastern boundary north of Ardnamurchan is generally recognised by its associated scarp, and a small flat-topped outlier of plateau basalt has been identified north-east of Eigg.

Some 7 km to the south-west of Mull, a small outlier of basalt has been tentatively mapped from its character on shallow-seismic profiles (BGS Tiree Solid Geology sheet). Sampling of this outlier has resulted in the recovery of a predominance of intrusive igneous rocks (Barber et al., 1979), and it may be that the few basalt samples are fine-grained intrusive rocks rather than lavas.

Farther south-west in the Colonsay Basin (Figure 4), it has been inferred from a deep-seismic section that a thin basalt

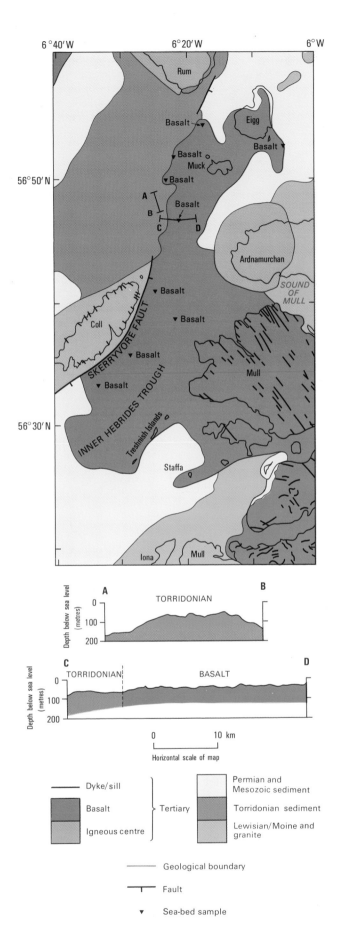

Figure 40 Geological map showing the distribution of basalt to the west of Mull, and including two bathymetric profiles from Eden et al. (1971).

layer lies beneath Tertiary sediments (Evans et al., 1979). The extent of the possible basalt identified in the Colonsay Basin is uncertain, but no basalts have been mapped adjacent to the Blackstones Bank igneous centre (BGS Tiree Solid Geology sheet).

ANTRIM

The largely basaltic lavas of Antrim (Figure 3) form the largest onshore area of extrusive rock in the BTVP, and although their preserved maximum thickness is thought to be some 800 m, they may originally have been as thick as those on Mull (Wilson, 1972). The Lower Basalt Formation of alkali-olivine type occurs mainly to the south of the Tow Valley Fault, but is also found at the north coast and on Rathlin Island. Its eruption was followed by a period of relative quiescence with only limited volcanicity, during which some rhyolites and the Causeway Tholeiites of the Giant's Causeway were erupted. Prolonged deep weathering of the top surface of the Lower Basalt Formation produced the distinctive red colouration of the Interbasaltic Formation. Finally came the Upper Basalt Formation, most of which is preserved north of the Tow Valley Fault, which was undergoing contemporaneous movement (Wilson, 1972).

The distribution pattern of the lavas is closely reflected by high-frequency aeromagnetic anomalies (BGS Malin Aeromagnetic Anomaly sheet). This observation, combined with knowledge of the coastal geology and seismic interpretation, indicates that the lavas do not extend more than a short distance offshore in the North Channel (BGS Clyde and Malin Solid Geology sheets). Along the north coast of Antrim, the outcrop of the magnetic anomalies is diffused by the presence of plugs and other minor intrusions within Mesozoic rocks beyond the outcrop of the lavas (BGS Malin Solid Geology sheet). Nevertheless, using seismic and bathymetric information, the extent of the lavas can be accurately identified a few kilometres north of the coast. In the area north of the Giant's Causeway and Benbane Head (Figures 3 and 37), the limit of basalt is marked by a well-defined bathymetric scarp (Evans et al., 1979a, fig. 9), but to the east, and more particularly to the west of Portrush, the topographic difference between the lava and older sediments diminishes. Rathlin Island has been shown to be an isolated outlier of basalt; strong scarps occur to the north and east, but not to the south within Rathlin Sound (Evans et al., 1979a, fig. 15). The plugs identified to the north (Durant, 1979) may have been important feeders for the lavas, which perhaps once extended significantly farther north than at present (Evans et al., 1979).

Intrusive igneous centres

Igneous centres occur on Skye, Rum, Ardnamurchan, Mull, and Arran, as well as at the Blackstones Bank. Of these, only the Blackstones Bank centre occurs exclusively under the sea, although the patterns of high Bouguer gravity anomalies over the Ardnamurchan (Bott and Tuson, 1973) and Rum centres suggest that both extend offshore (Figure 5).

In addition to the Blackstones Bank igneous centre, two large granitic bodies have been mapped to the west of Islay (Figure 3; BGS Malin Solid Geology sheet). The eastern body, 20 km west of Islay, is identified from its associated low Bouguer gravity anomaly (BGS Malin Bouguer Gravity Anomaly sheet). Its age is unknown, but its lack of topographic expression and occurrence within basement rocks may indicate that it is pre-Mesozoic. The western body, the

Malin Complex, lies outside the report area on the line of the Great Glen fault system (BGS Malin Solid Geology sheet). It may well be Tertiary, as it is apparently intruded into sediments which are thought to be of Mesozoic age (Evans et al., 1979). Seismic profiling indicates some rockhead irregularity over the body (Evans, 1974). Riddihough (1968) interpreted the Malin Complex as a granitic ring structure on the basis of its oval magnetic high with a central low, perhaps accompanied by a minor gravity low.

BLACKSTONES BANK IGNEOUS CENTRE

The Blackstones Bank igneous centre forms an area with irregular, high relief (Figure 41; Eden et al., 1971), and was described by McQuillin et al. (1975) from gravity, magnetic and seismic data. The area is not a very strongly defined regional bathymetric high because the Mesozoic rocks surrounding the body have a thick cover of Quaternary, and locally Tertiary, sediments. The centre is coincident with a very large positive Bouguer gravity anomaly up to +154 mGal, that has a slightly oval shape (Figure 5). McQuillin et al. (1975) modelled the anomaly as approximating to a vertical cylinder of basic and ultrabasic rock 16 km in diameter extending to near the base of the crust at 22 to 30 km, thus supporting an earlier unpublished interpretation by Faruquee (1972). The intrusion produces an oval, north-north-westerly orientated, negative magnetic anomaly, and seismic-reflection records show rugged topography that forms a strongly reflecting surface overlying a seismically structureless interior.

The mapped boundaries of the centre form a north-north-westerly orientated oval with a large embayment along its north-eastern side (Figure 41). Mesozoic and Tertiary sediments partly overlie the intrusion, but are faulted on the north-western margin of the embayment (McQuillin et al., 1975). Samples from bedrock pinnacles which approach to within 20 m of the sea surface have been collected by divers (Durant et al., 1982); the wide variety of rock types sampled, and the common presence of two or more lithologies per site, testify to the complex nature of the centre. The samples indicate that the bulk of the outcrop is formed from gabbros which exhibit a wide variation in texture and mineralogy. The mineral compositions vary from outcrop to outcrop, and may indicate either different intrusions or different parts of an intrusion which shows a marked cryptic variation in phase compositions. Many samples show clinopyroxene-, olivine-, and most particularly plagioclase-cumulate textures produced by crystallisation and accumulation within a magma chamber. However, no evidence has been found of major olivine-rich units of the type forming substantial parts of the Eastern Layered Series of Rum, where thick peridotitic layers and overlying plagioclase-rich (allivalite) layers occur in repeated succession (Wager and Brown, 1968). Peridotite is more susceptible to weathering than allivalite, and differential erosion may account for resistant plagioclase-rich rocks forming the shallowest peaks on the Blackstones Bank shoal.

The area of gabbro outcrop is crossed by gullies formed by the preferential erosion of minor basaltic intrusions, resulting in spectacular and rugged underwater scenery. Basaltic dykes and inclined sheets cutting gabbro or granite were recorded at virtually every site, but no lavas were found. Granitic rocks within the main body, found either as small stocks or as veins cutting gabbro, produce a more subdued topography. Granophyre forms an extensive outcrop on the north-eastern side of the bank, and a microgranite was discovered in the south-east.

Heat from the intrusion has metamorphosed calcareous shales, probably of Mesozoic age, to produce calcsilicate hornfels with diopside, garnet, idocrase, monticellite and spinel.

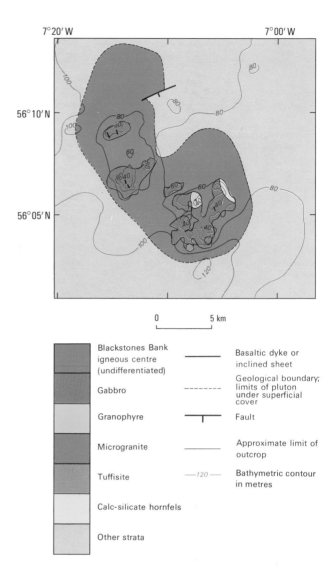

Figure 41 Outcrop map of the Blackstones Bank igneous centre. For location see Figure 4.

Undated calcareous metasediments were sampled at sites within the centre, but close to its eastern margin. These, along with one small fragment of quartzite, almost certainly represent the country rocks into which the centre was emplaced.

The first dating of a sample from the centre by Durant et al. (1976) gave a minimum age of 70 Ma, which would place the intrusive event in the Late Cretaceous. Subsequently, Mitchell et al. (1976) published dates from dredged basalt samples which had a mean age of 57.1 ±0.9 Ma (Paleocene). Later dating of feldspars from Durant's in-situ samples has produced comparable ages of 58.4, 58.6 and 58.8 Ma (all ±1.2 Ma), which appear to confirm that the Blackstones Bank igneous centre is coeval with other early Tertiary centres in the Hebrides (BGS Tiree Solid Geology sheet).

Smaller intrusions

Igneous intrusions can only be recognised on seismic-reflection records where they are of a significantly different acoustic character to that of the country rock. Where they intrude softer Mesozoic strata, they can be identified from their strongly reflecting surface, their lack of internal structure, and their topographic expression either at sea bed or beneath drift. Dyke swarms and concentrations of other minor intrusions can be detected from aeromagnetic data, and smaller intrusions produce anomalies on marine magnetic traces. Dykes

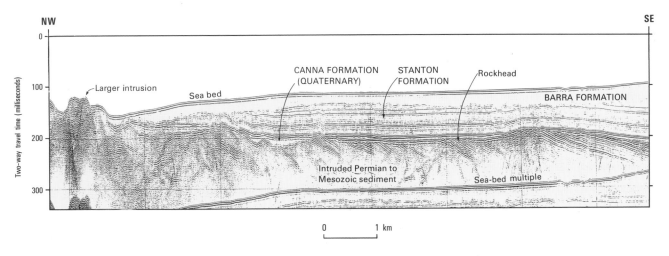

Figure 42 Annotated sparker profile from the Sea of the Hebrides-Little Minch Trough. Within the Mesozoic sediments, dykes show as hyperbolic reflections. For location see Figure 38.

are generally too thin to be resolved on seismic records, but can form point-source hyperbolic reflectors within softer rock (Figure 42); nevertheless they are very difficult to trace between seismic lines and their distribution has not been mapped in the report area. Minor intrusions can rarely be traced on seismic records where they intrude basement rocks, and in these circumstances their magnetic character may also be hidden. To date, insufficient work has been done to clearly relate dykes to individual igneous centres, but some geographical links can be made.

THE NORTH MINCH BASIN

The land around the North Minch Basin is generally devoid of Tertiary igneous intrusions, and the aeromagnetic map shows that the Mesozoic rocks offshore are for the most part magnetically subdued (Figure 6; BGS Lewis and Sutherland Aeromagnetic Anomaly sheets), indicating a similar absence. Exceptions are the area of high-frequency magnetic anomalies

in the extreme north-west of the report area, and the strongly defined 110 km-long Minch Anomaly trending north-north-west from Loch Maree (Figure 6). A similarly orientated, though shorter, magnetic anomaly occurs outside the report area north-west of Lewis (Ofoegbu and Bott, 1985), and a broader zone of anomalies crosses Lewis from Loch Roag to an area south-east of the Shiant Islands. The latter were related by Watson (1977) to a dyke swarm.

The magnetic anomalies in the far north-west are considered to be produced by minor basic intrusions which form very localised and subdued bathymetric highs that have been sampled at two localities as altered olivine-dolerite and altered tholeiitic basalt of presumed early Tertiary age (BGS Sutherland Solid Geology sheet).

The Minch Anomaly is such a startling magnetic feature (Figure 6) that it was the subject of the first ever BGS marine investigation in 1966 (Fannin, 1989). Ofoegbu and Bott (1985) related this feature to a dyke with an average, and fairly

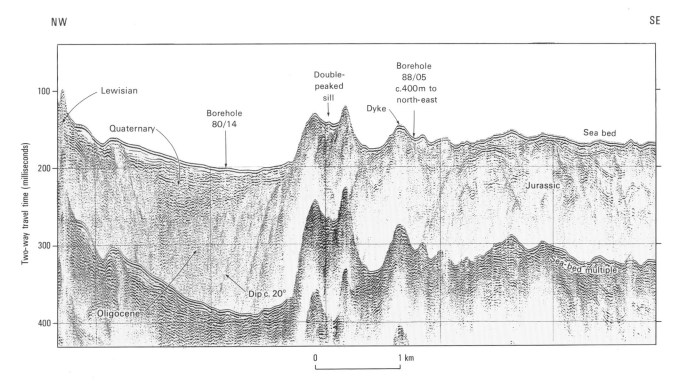

Figure 43 Annotated sparker profile from the Little Minch. For location see Figure 38.

constant width, of about 1.1 km. The dyke does not crop out, and the depth to the top of the dyke varies from 0.3 km to over 2 km. This particularly large dyke is intruded into Permo-Triassic and Jurassic sediments and is most probably of early Tertiary age. Ofoegbu and Bott (1985) concluded that the dyke was intruded as the result of approximately east–west extension. To the north of Skye, these stresses produced a few wide dykes, in contrast to the numerous narrow dykes farther south. The Minch Anomaly dyke may be related either to the Skye centre or to the thick pile of lavas at the Wyville–Thomson Ridge (Ofoegbu and Bott, 1985; Roberts et al., 1983)

SEA OF THE HEBRIDES–LITTLE MINCH TROUGH

This area includes the western part of the Isle of Skye, where a wide variety of sills, dykes, plugs and vents are found (Richey, 1961). Offshore, dykes are recognised on seismic profiles, and many larger intrusions have been identified (Figure 42), although very few have been sampled and no details of their subsurface structure are known.

In the north, the Shiant Islands sill complex (Gibb and Henderson, 1984) is a thick, differentiated basic sheet that has been mapped over a wide area under the sea adjacent to the islands (Figure 38). Several other intrusions likely to re-semble either the Shiant structure or the olivine-dolerites of the Madadh Rocks (McKinnon, 1974) have been traced. The few good sea-bed samples obtained have proved to be meso-cratic, medium-grained dolerites, and off southern Harris, BGS borehole 88/05 (Figures 38 and 43) recovered 1.10 m of coarse-grained, equigranular dolerite displaying subophitic texture. It was K-Ar dated at 52.2 to 57.6 Ma, indicating a latest Paleocene to early Eocene age for the intrusion (Snelling, 1987).

Larger minor intrusions are less common in the Sea of the Hebrides–Little Minch Trough between 56°50'N and 57°30'N, where they tend to occur towards the Minch Fault (Figure 42). The only bedrock sample obtained from the area proved to be a decomposed tuff with feldspar, muscovite, al-tered biotite and granular iron in an argillaceous matrix (Binns et al., 1974b). In the southern part of the trough, minor intru-sions are again common, and by comparison with the north-ern part of this region, are assumed to be basic intrusive rocks.

Dykes and other minor intrusions are found on Rum and Coll, and probably lie undetected within the Torridonian and Lewisian rocks offshore. However, there is nothing on the aeromagnetic map to suggest that the Mull dyke swarm ex-tends significantly to the north-west of Mull (Figure 6).

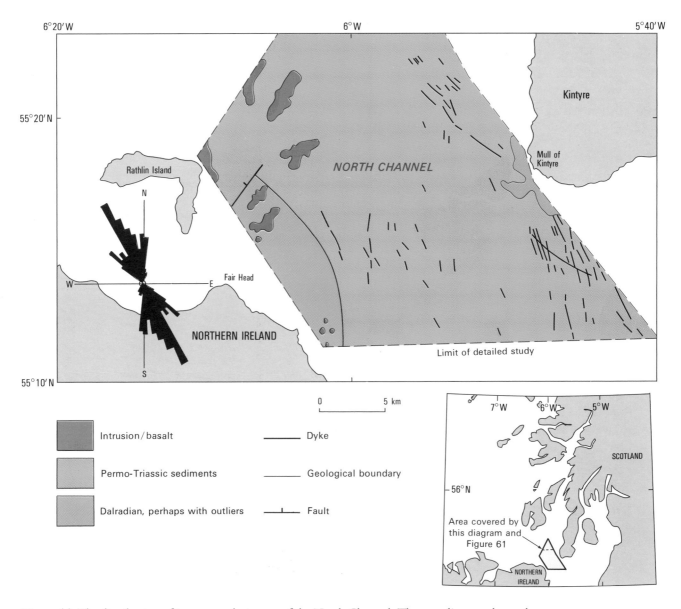

Figure 44 The distribution of igneous rocks in part of the North Channel. The rose diagram shows the orientations of dykes in the area of detailed study.

INNER HEBRIDES TROUGH AND MALIN BASIN

To the north of Ardnamurchan, the Mesozoic rocks of the Inner Hebrides Trough are heavily intruded. A similar pattern is found south of the Mull basalts, where some intrusions are large (BGS Tiree Solid Geology sheet). The islet of Dubh Artach is part of a 15 km-long, south-south-westerly striking, sill-like body formed of coarsely ophitic dolerite that has been sampled in BGS borehole 72/12 (Figures 1 and 3). To the south-west of Blackstones Bank, two ill-defined basic intrusions have been identified (Figure 3), and a number of minor intrusions have been mapped farther south-west in the Malin Basin (BGS Malin Solid Geology sheet).

On the Blackstones Bank igneous centre, basaltic dykes and inclined sheets have been identified because they have been preferentially eroded to form large gullies (Durant, 1979). Intrusions of granophyre, microgranite and tuffisite have also been recognised within the complex (Figure 41; BGS Tiree Solid Geology sheet).

COLONSAY BASIN

This region includes the Firth of Lorne, which is crossed by the Mull dyke swarm. An outcrop of a dyke from this swarm was observed during a submersible dive (Eden et al., 1971). Few specific intrusions have been mapped, for harder pre-Mesozoic rocks dominate, but like the adjacent land areas, it is undoubtedly extensively intruded. Sampling by divers has produced several examples of Tertiary igneous rocks from these minor intrusions (Barber et al., 1979; Durant, 1979).

ISLAY TO NORTHERN IRELAND.

In the north of this region, linear magnetic anomalies mark the Islay–Jura dyke swarm (Walker, 1959), which has been identified offshore to the west of Kintyre (Figure 6) by McLean and Deegan (1978). Intrusions are uncommon in the Permo-Triassic and Jurassic rocks of the Loch Indaal Basin and the northern part of the Rathlin Trough (Figure 28), both of which show subdued magnetic anomaly character, but are abundant in the more southerly part of the Rathlin Trough (Evans et al., 1979). Sea-bed pinnacles north of the Antrim

coast have been sampled by dredging (Durant, 1979); most appear to be medium- or coarse-grained, intrusive, basic rocks, although the sample from the horseshoe-shaped Laconia Bank (Figure 2) is pyroclastic. Evans et al. (1979) speculated that these bodies may have been lava feeders for the Antrim basalts, and would therefore be analogous to onshore plugs, such as that at Slemish in County Antrim (Preston, 1963).

THE FIRTH OF CLYDE REGION

McLean and Deegan (1978) report numerous dykes in the Firth of Clyde region, particularly off the south coast of Arran. Several larger intrusions west of Troon (Figures 1 and 3) compare with thick, crinanitic, laccolithic sills of Tertiary age in Ayrshire (Armstrong, 1957; Mykura, 1967). A linear magnetic anomaly, termed the Ailsa Craig line (Figure 6), extends from Ailsa Craig to the south coast of Arran. A series of minor bathymetric pinnacles along this line (Figure 2) are probably expressions of small, plug-like igneous bodies which are the near-surface manifestations of a much larger basic mass in the upper crust forming a link between Ailsa Craig,, comprising Tertiary riebeckite microgranite, and the Arran igneous centre (McLean and Wren, 1978). Two boreholes drilled in the vicinity of Ailsa Craig (Figure 1) recovered igneous rocks; 72/04 apparently penetrated the edge of an igneous body, and 72/05 recovered a coarsely ophitic dolerite containing phenocrysts of olivine and plagioclase (Deegan, 1978).

In a detailed study of sidescan sonar records, it has been found that the dykes between Fair Head and the Mull of Kintyre in the North Channel have a well-defined north-north-westerly orientation (Figure 44). These dykes can form 'walls' up to 9 m in height above the tidally scoured sea bed (Figure 45). In the more central part of the North Channel, Caston (1975; 1976) identified many dykes with a similar trend, and up to 28 m high.

MIDDLE TERTIARY SEDIMENTS

Following the volcanic episode, the late Eocene and early Oligocene were times of uplift and erosion in the north-west

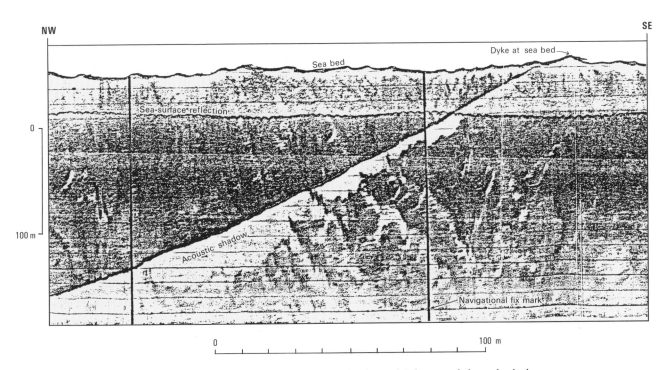

Figure 45 Sidescan sonar record of a dyke at outcrop in the North Channel. The record shows both the profile of the sea floor and a swath across which the dyke forms an upstanding wall at the sea bed.

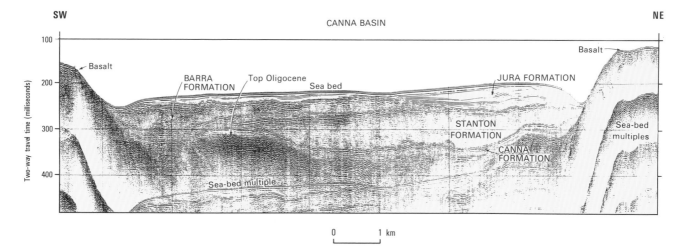

Figure 46 Sparker profile across the Canna Basin. For location see Figure 38.

British Isles. The products of this erosion during the late Eocene were largely washed into the subsiding Rockall Trough. On the shelf, localised subsidence led to the accumulation and preservation of terrestrial, late Oligocene sediments. Three such outliers have been identified offshore in the Malin–Hebrides area: the Canna Basin, the Blackstones Basin, and a small occurrence in the Little Minch. Direct evidence from these basins is relatively sparse, but the terrestrial sediments of the Lough Neagh Basin (Wilkinson et al., 1980) in Northern Ireland were also laid down at this time, and provide a depositional model which can perhaps be applied to the offshore sequences.

The distribution of the Lough Neagh Clays (Wilkinson et al., 1980) today is probably considerably less extensive than was the subsiding freshwater lake in which they were deposited during the late Oligocene. The sediments, which have a maximum proven thickness of 380 m, are predominantly pale- to medium-grey clays and silty clays, with common development of lignites which can be up to 80 m thick (Geological Survey of Northern Ireland, 1984). Pebble beds occur in the west, implying that the rivers carrying the sediment came from that direction, although the presence of sands to the north-east also suggests minor input from that direction. The rivers were draining an area that included shallow lagoons which supported the luxuriant tropical vegetation that provided carbonaceous material to form the lignites. Later mid-Tertiary faulting has been a major influence in determining the present extent of the sediments (George, 1967). Recently, drilling has led to the discovery of three small faulted basins of very similar lignite-rich sediments on the north side of the Tow Valley Fault (Figure 37), some 40 km north of Lough Neagh (Griffith et al., 1987)

Little Minch

The most northerly known occurrence of terrestrial Oligocene sediments to the west of the British Isles is a restricted basin that lies in the Little Minch adjacent to the Minch Fault (Figures 38 and 43). From it, BGS borehole 80/14 proved pale to dark grey, commonly carbonaceous mudstone with lignites and thin, gritty, poorly sorted sandstone beds (Evans et al., 1991). The carbonaceous material is composed of plant fragments and wood, and the sediments contain abundant pollen with strong similarities to other western UK late Oligocene terrestrial basins. The pollen proved a Chattian to Stampian age for the sediments, which were deposited in a floodplain environment dominated by

complexes of arborescent swamps and fens. The sandstones, which may represent crevasse-splay deposits, are largely derived from higher-grade crystalline metamorphic basement, probably from the Lewisian to the west. The minor presence of Jurassic pollen and reworked glaucony indicates reworking of Jurassic rocks, either from the Inner Hebrides to the east, or perhaps from a source in the west.

Seismic data (Figure 43) show the sediments to be relatively steeply dipping and lying above a Tertiary sill, and perhaps bounded to the north-west by the Minch Fault. The relationships of the sediment to the Minch Fault are not sufficiently clear to establish post-Oligocene movement on the fault. The basin cannot be confidently traced laterally beyond the very restricted area shown on Figure 38, but the possibility of other small basins occurring adjacent to the Minch Fault has been confirmed by the results of BGS borehole 88/12, which recovered almost 13 m of interbedded conglomerate, sandstone and mudstone. The conglomerate contains clasts of basalt that have yielded K-Ar ages of 59.8 ± 1.3 Ma, and palynological investigations of the mudstone (J Thomas, written communication, 1991) indicate a Tertiary assemblage, as well as Jurassic forms. A latest Paleocene or younger age is therefore proposed for the sediments, whose extent is unknown, but probably very limited.

Canna Basin

The existence of Tertiary sediments in the Canna Basin was first postulated on geophysical grounds by Smythe and Kenolty (1975), who recognised a north-easterly trending, pear-shaped basin (Figure 38). The sediments may be up to 1000 m thick, and lie within a downwarp of the Tertiary basalts (Figure 12); they are gently folded and are overlain with marked unconformity by Quaternary sediments (Figure 46). From the structural setting, thickness and calculated density of the sediment, Smythe and Kenolty (1975) inferred that the Canna Basin is infilled with lacustrine sediments of Oligocene age similiar to those of the Lough Neagh Basin. Subsequently, BGS borehole 78/01 (Figure 38) drilled 19.1 m of dark brownish grey, stiff to very hard, silty, carbonaceous clay with plant remains and lignitic fragments, interbedded with dark bluish grey, carbonaceous, micaceous siltstone (Evans et al., 1979b). Basic igneous pebbles and brown-stained quartz grains are common throughout the sequence. Samples contain no marine dinoflagellate cysts or calcareous microfossils, but have pollen assemblages that confirm a Chattian age contemporaneous with that of the Lough Neagh Clays. The sediments were deposited in a brackish-nearshore or lacustrine environment with an influx of plant debris and coarser sediment.

Blackstones and Colonsay basins

From their interpretation of the Canna Basin, Smythe and Kenolty (1975) established a series of criteria to differentiate Tertiary sediments from those of Mesozoic age. The criteria included low interval velocity, evenly spaced reflectors on sparker records, transparency on deep-seismic profiles, an absence of intrusions, and folding and/or faulting to differentiate from Quaternary deposits. They considered that these criteria were met by sediments covering a large area east of the Blackstones Bank in the Blackstones Basin, the adjacent Colonsay Basin, and a third area south-east of Tiree. Further mapping suggests that only the first two are Tertiary basins (Figures 3 and 4; BGS Tiree Solid Geology sheet), but no samples have been obtained from them. Regional considerations suggest that they are likely to be terrestrial deposits of late Oligocene age, although Smythe and Kenolty (1975) originally suggested that they might be marine sediments

The Blackstones Basin is a generally north–south-trending, irregularly shaped basin. In its northern part, the sediment can be seen on sparker records to be gently folded, and not intruded. The infilling sediment is faulted against the north-easterly trending Skerryvore Fault in the north, indicating late movement on that fault. In the north-east, the sediments overlie a large, westerly dipping sill of coarsely ophitic dolerite (BGS Tiree Solid Geology sheet). The unknown thickness of Tertiary probably rests directly on Mesozoic sediment and/or the sill. In the west, the sediment overlies, or is faulted against, the Blackstones Bank igneous centre, but limits have not been identified in the south-west and south-east because the Quaternary cover is too thick for the underlying sediment to be identified on shallow-seismic profiles.

In the adjacent Colonsay Basin, possible Oligocene sediments that may be a continuation of those of the Blackstones Basin lie under the thick Quaternary cover which obscures the basin margins in the north-east and south-west. The south-eastern extent of the Oligocene sediments can be seen on a deep-seismic profile as coincident with the Colonsay Fault. Evans et al. (1979a) showed the Tertiary sediments up to 400 m thick and overlying a thin, faulted, basalt layer which caps the Mesozoic succession. On sparker records, the Tertiary sediments image as gently folded reflectors underlying the base-Quaternary unconformity at about 250 m below sea bed.

10 Quaternary

The Quaternary Period, which comprises the Pleistocene and Holocene epochs, has been a time of dramatic changes in climatic conditions. It has included intervals of severe erosion by glacial processes, rapid changes in sea level, and very high sedimentation rates. The land around the Malin–Hebrides sea area was probably subjected to subaerial erosion from late Tertiary to early Pleistocene times, but during the later Quaternary, decreasing temperature permitted the development of glaciers on the high mountains. As these spread, they caused both erosion and deposition on a large scale. Offshore, their main legacy has been glaciomarine deposits that locally exceed 300 m in thickness in glacially eroded basins (Figure 47). The former presence of grounded ice has been confirmed by observations of morainic mounds and glacial striae on submarine rock exposures (Eden et al., 1971).

The report area is characterised by considerable sea-bed relief, and the rockhead in some of the deep, elongate rock basins descends to more than 400 m below sea level. The rock basins tend to form over Mesozoic or younger sedimentary strata, whereas the intervening ridges are composed either of Precambrian or Tertiary igneous rocks. The occurrence of Tertiary sediments within depressions adjacent to tracts of positive relief formed by Tertiary volcanic rock (Smythe and Kenolty, 1975) indicates that part of the relief is Tertiary in origin (Evans et al., 1982). However, the extreme overdeepening of many of the basins and their general orientation in sympathy with suggested ice-flow directions implies that glacial erosion has been an important agent in the development of the rockhead morphology (Sutherland, 1984).

The resistant ridges which separate the basins commonly display irregular outcrop topography. The Quaternary deposits that infill the basins are therefore restricted in area and isolated from each other (Figure 47). This pattern contrasts strongly with the large, extensive and laterally continuous Quaternary basin of the North Sea. The lowermost sediments in the report area probably date from the pre-Devensian, but the major part is of late Devensian age. This again contrasts with the North Sea, where a tectonically subsiding basin has allowed the preservation of thick early Pleistocene marine or deltaic sediments, as well as the deposits of more than one subsequent glaciation (Cameron et al., 1987).

The relatively thin Quaternary sediments on the land adjacent to the report area have been studied for over a century, and it is apparent that most were deposited during late Devensian times. Early studies of the offshore Quaternary reported only sediments of late Devensian and younger age for the inner shelf also (Deegan et al., 1973; Binns et al., 1974a; Bishop and Jones, 1979; Evans et al., 1980;). However, more recent work by Davies et al. (1984) and BGS mapping (see inside back cover) have suggested seismic stratigraphies including considerable thicknesses of sediments predating the late Devensian. Indeed, the Quaternary succession of the Hebrides is presently thought to include at least two formations that predate the Devensian.

However, there has been little direct dating of offshore sediments. A few radiocarbon determinations have been made on the youngest units in boreholes 71/09 and 78/04 (Harkness and Wilson, 1974; Graham et al., 1990), and four unpublished BGS amino-acid racemisation measurements are available. Unlike the North Sea successions (Cameron et al., 1984), palaeomagnetic determinations have not yet aided chronostratigraphical interpretation, but micropalaeontological analyses carried out by BGS biostratigraphers have identified cold and warmer episodes, which have been used together with the seismostratigraphy to suggest ages for the Quaternary sediments. The dearth of dating has restricted chronostratigraphical subdivision into pre-late Devensian and late Devensian successions.

The report area can be subdivided into three main regions in which evidence of Quaternary deposition is preserved; the Minch succession is effectively separated from the Sea of the Hebrides deposits at the Rubha Reidh Ridge, and the Firth of Clyde sequence is isolated by the absence of Quaternary in the North Channel (Figure 47). Within each of these regions there may be individual basins between which direct reflector correlation is generally not possible, although similarities in seismic-reflection signature and architecture may be recognised.

Different seismostratigraphies have been established north and south of the Rubha Reidh Ridge (Figure 48). Within The Minch, an informal seismostratigraphy has been developed by BGS (Lewis Quaternary Geology sheet; Sutherland Sea Bed Sediments and Quaternary Geology sheet). In the Hebridean region, the early four-formation stratigraphy of Binns et al. (1974a) has been superseded by the more detailed work of Davies et al. (1984). No stratigraphy has yet been established within the Firth of Clyde region.

PRE-LATE DEVENSIAN

Like the later part of the Tertiary, the beginning of the Quaternary was a time of denudation of the land surrounding the report area, and it is likely that erosion also took place offshore. Unlike the North Sea, where substantial thicknesses of lower Pleistocene sediments are preserved, the area shows no evidence of tectonic subsidence. The lowermost Quaternary sediments identified may date from the pre-Devensian, but any preglacial deposits would probably have been eroded by glacial activity.

The Minch region

The Quaternary succession at Toa Galson (Lowe, 1984; Sutherland and Walker, 1984) in northern Lewis (Figure 49) has been used by Sutherland (1984) to summarise pre-late Devensian events on the Outer Hebrides. There is evidence that an early episode of marine erosion of bedrock formed the raised rock platform at about 9 m above OD, to be followed by glaciation of the whole of northern Lewis. Subsequently, there was a time of mild, possibly interglacial conditions during which a peat dated as greater than 47 150 years BP was formed. Pollen in the peat show that the essentially treeless vegetation progressively changed from grasses and sedges to acid heathland. Next, the site was subjected to severely cold conditions with frost shattering and solifluction, before beach

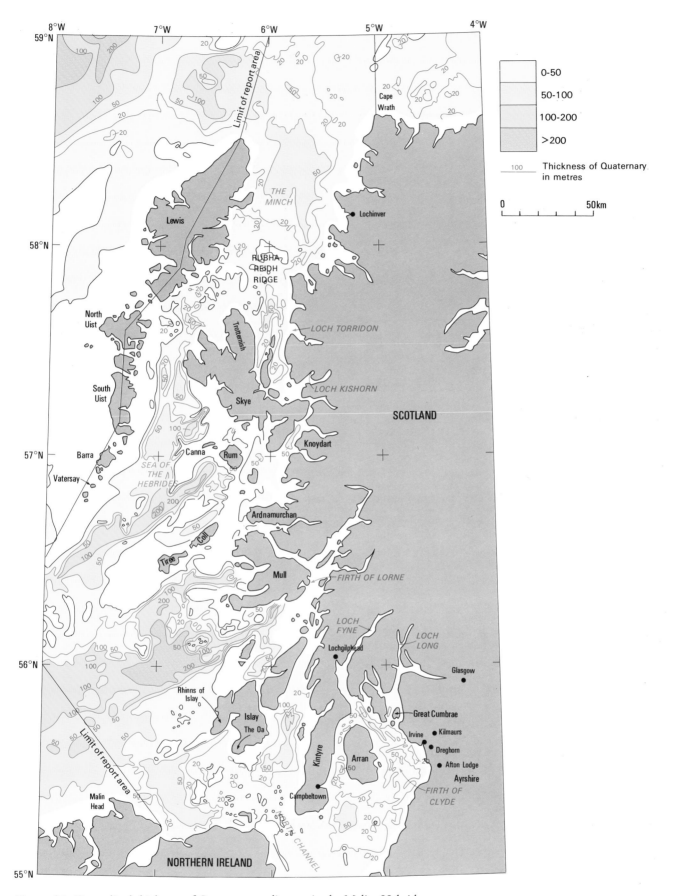

Figure 47 Generalised thickness of Quaternary sediments in the Malin–Hebrides area.

59

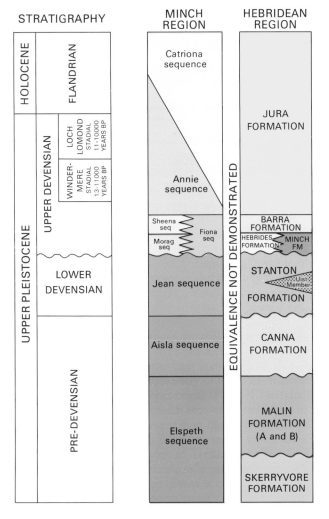

Figure 48 Quaternary stratigraphies for the Malin–Hebrides area. The Minch region lies to the north of the Rubha Reidh Ridge, and the Hebridean region to the south. No offshore stratigraphy has been established for the Firth of Clyde region.

gravels, which occur at up to 12 m above OD, were deposited while late Devensian ice covered other parts of northern Lewis (Sutherland and Walker, 1984).

Other pre-late Devensian deposits in northern Lewis have been identified at Tolsta Head (Figure 49; Lowe, 1984), where an interstadial organic deposit laid down in a cool, deteriorating climate (Birnie, 1983) has been dated as 27 333 ± 240 years BP (von Weymarn and Edwards, 1973). Also, beach gravels similar to those at Toa Galson have been identified beneath till on Barra and Vatersay (Figure 47) at the southern end of the Outer Hebrides (Peacock, 1984; Selby, 1987).

Offshore, BGS (Lewis Quaternary Geology sheet; Sutherland Sea Bed Sediments and Quaternary Geology sheet) has established a separate Quaternary stratigraphy to that of the Hebridean region (Figure 48). Deposits around the margin of The Minch have been mapped as undifferentiated Quaternary as they cannot be clearly assigned to a seismic sequence, but as this unit thickens away from the margins, the succession revealed on seismic profiles can be separated into seismostratigraphical sequences. Generally the stratigraphical range increases, and the surface deposits become older, towards the north-west, where the Minch supersequence merges into the Clan supersequence on the outer shelf. This suggests repeated erosion on the inner shelf, nearer to the ice-sheet sources.

ELSPETH SEQUENCE

This, the lowest mapped sequence in the region, crops out at the sea bed north and north-west of the Butt of Lewis outside the report area, but locally subcrops at the report boundary (Figure 49). On seismic profiles it is generally rather featureless and transparent, but contains sporadic, impersistent reflectors where it thickens to more than 100 m locally in the south-east of the North Lewis Basin. In borehole 77/08, the sequence consists of up to 20 m of reddish brown, stiff, sandy, silty clay with pebbles. The lithology and the foraminiferal content of the sequence indicate glaciomarine deposition, and its stratigraphical position suggests that it may predate the late Devensian (BGS Lewis Quaternary Geology sheet). Amino-acid racemisation results on *Elphidium excavatum* (Terquem) cf *clavata* Cushman yielded a result of 0.175, which would suggest a Saalian or older age for the Elspeth sequence in BGS borehole 77/08.

AISLA SEQUENCE

Overlying the Elspeth sequence is the Aisla sequence, a predominantly seismically structureless or chaotic unit that tends to transparency. It occurs in the north-west of the North Minch Basin (Figure 49), thickening westwards to 40 m north of the Butt of Lewis where it crops out over a limited area. The sequence occurs as a patchy remnant beyond its mapped limit over much of the North Minch Basin (Figures 50 and 51). The top is eroded, and is characteristically markedly uneven, except where it is overlain by the Jean sequence. This erosion surface is attributed to action during the late Devensian glacial maximum (BGS Sutherland Sea Bed Sediment and Quaternary Geology sheet), an interpretation influenced by the identification of a major late Devensian erosion surface above the Stanton Formation in the Hebridean region (Davies et al., 1984). However, this northern surface may be older. In either case, a pre-late Devensian age can be assigned to the Aisla sequence. The sequence has been sampled in borehole 77/08 (Figure 49) where the dark grey, silty, sandy and pebbly clay with shell fragments is considered to be glaciomarine in origin (BGS Sutherland Sea Bed Sediments and Quaternary Geology sheet). A 5 m section sampled in BGS borehole 76/55 comprises very dark grey, soft to firm, sandy clay with few pebbles.

JEAN SEQUENCE

The Jean sequence occurs to the north of the Butt of Lewis (Figure 49) where it is up to 40 m thick. It is featureless or slightly transparent on seismic-reflection records, with a generally well-defined base and top. The base lies unconformably upon either bedrock or the Aisla sequence in the North Minch Basin, but upon older Quaternary units in the North Lewis Basin. The top generally shows a major erosion surface developed prior to the deposition of the Morag sequence; this is attributed to late Devensian, or perhaps earlier, glaciation. The sequence was drilled in borehole 77/08 where it comprises soft to stiff, dark to very dark grey, pebbly and slightly sandy, silty clay that contains an arctic-like microfauna. The lithology and fauna together indicate glaciomarine sedimentation in 20 to 50 m of water with seasonal or permanent sea-ice.

The Hebridean region

No deposits of pre-Devensian age are known on land around this region, but raised marine-erosion features at many sites in the Inner Hebrides are considered to be the result of rapid cutting in a periglacial climate (Dawson, 1980). These occur most notably on Mull, Jura and Islay, and have been assigned

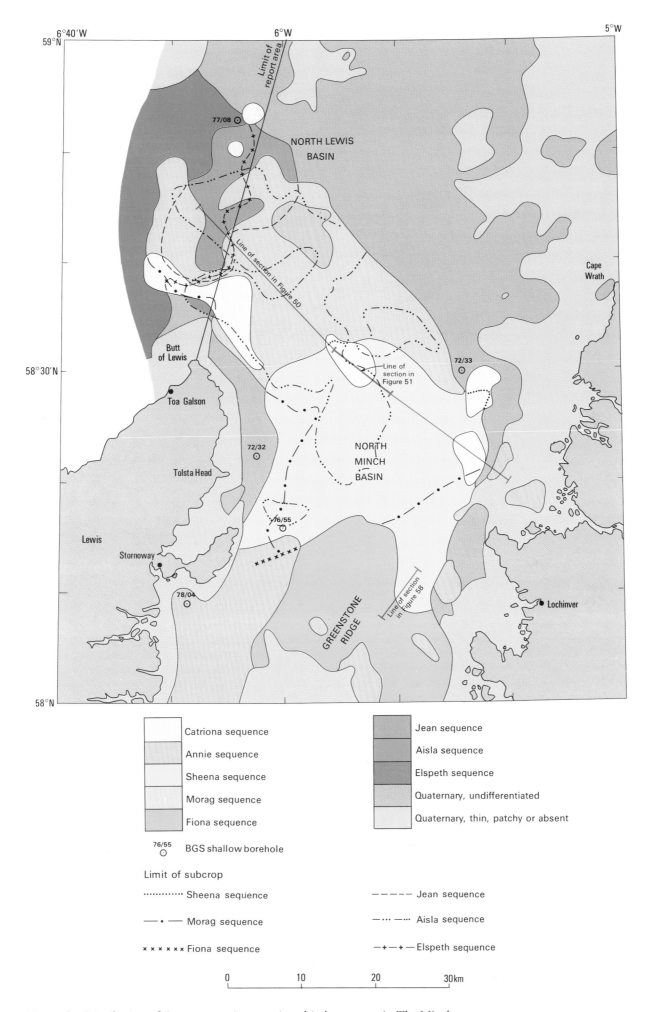

Figure 49 Distribution of Quaternary seismostratigraphical sequences in The Minch.

The following labels appear on the map:

6°40'W · 6°W · 5°W
59°N · 58°30'N · 58°N

Limit of report area

77/08

NORTH LEWIS BASIN

Cape Wrath

Line of section in Figure 50

Line of section in Figure 51

72/33

Butt of Lewis

Toa Galson

72/32

NORTH MINCH BASIN

Tolsta Head

76/55

Lewis

Stornoway

Line of section in Figure 58

78/04

Lochinver

GREENSTONE RIDGE

Legend:

Catriona sequence
Annie sequence
Sheena sequence
Morag sequence
Fiona sequence

Jean sequence
Aisla sequence
Elspeth sequence
Quaternary, undifferentiated
Quaternary, thin, patchy or absent

76/55 ⊙ BGS shallow borehole

Limit of subcrop

·········· Sheena sequence
— • — Morag sequence
× × × × × Fiona sequence

— — — — Jean sequence
— ··· — ··· Aisla sequence
— + — + Elspeth sequence

0   10   20   30km

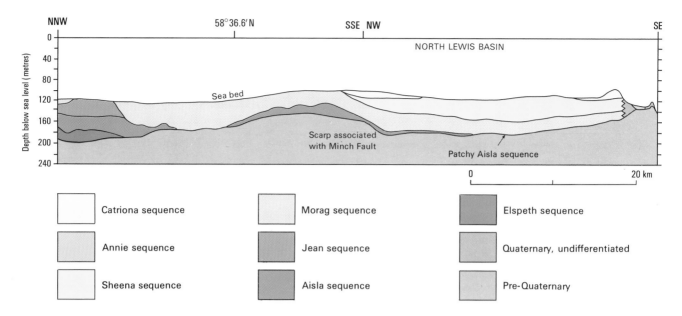

Figure 50 Cross-section showing the relationships of Quaternary sequences in The Minch. For location see Figure 49.

preglacial or interglacial ages; they may have been formed at any time when the crust was isostatically depressed during ice-sheet build up (Dawson, 1980). Similar pre-late Devensian rock platforms have been identified around the Firth of Clyde (Browne and McMillan, 1984), and a submerged wave-cut platform in the Firth of Lorne (Figure 47) may also predate the late Devensian (Hall and Rashid, 1977).

SKERRYVORE FORMATION

The oldest Quaternary sediments identified in this region are stiff silty clays up to 45 m thick that have a structureless seismic response, and are overlain conformably by up to 25 m of faintly, horizontally bedded sediments with diffraction hyperbolae indicating dropstones. Together, these two units have been termed the Skerryvore Formation (Davies et al., 1984) as they occur at depth chiefly to the south of Skerryvore, and possibly extend southwards into the Malin Sea (BGS Tiree Quaternary Geology sheet). The lower unit was sampled in borehole 81/10A (Figure 52); sediments from it yielded dinoflagellate cysts that were deposited under temperate, neritic conditions. The unsampled upper unit has been interpreted as a glaciomarine sediment due to the inferred presence of cobbles and boulders (Davies et al., 1984). These observations suggest that the Skerryvore Formation was deposited during a time of deteriorating climate, perhaps towards the close of an interstadial or interglacial. The dinoflagellate-cyst assemblage is dominated by *Achomosphaera andalouense* Jan

du Chêne; from his work in the North Sea, Harland (in Davies et al., 1984) believes the presence of this species may be indicative of the pre-Devensian.

MALIN FORMATION

Above the Skerryvore Formation (Figure 48) is the Malin Formation, which is best developed in the Malin Sea from where it derives its name, and where it has an average thickness of 75 m. It also occurs on the south-eastern margin of the Sea of the Hebrides–Little Minch Trough south of 57°N. Seismically, the formation has two distinct and laterally equivalent units that Davies et al. (1984) informally termed Malin A and Malin B (Figures 48 and 53).

Malin A is the more extensive of the two units, and is characterised by discontinuous reflectors, point-source diffraction patterns, and a hummocky upper surface. This combination of acoustic responses suggests that the unit is a stiff diamicton. This interpretation is confirmed by the lithology recovered in boreholes 81/10 and 81/10A, which comprise very stiff, dark grey, gravelly, sandy clay containing some small sand pods (Figure 52).

Malin B is characterised by parallel, subhorizontal, medium-spaced reflectors, and a general absence of diffraction hyperbolae. It generally occurs as small isolated pockets within or adjacent to Malin A (Figure 53), but in the Blackstones Basin it is developed as a separate large body that is apparently laterally equivalent to Malin A. Although no borehole con-

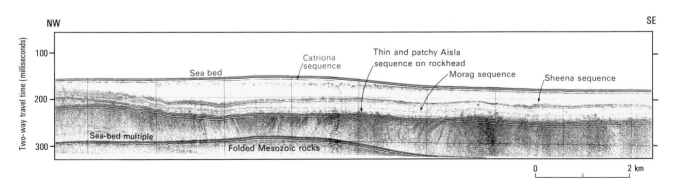

Figure 51 Annotated sparker profile from The Minch. For location see Figure 49.

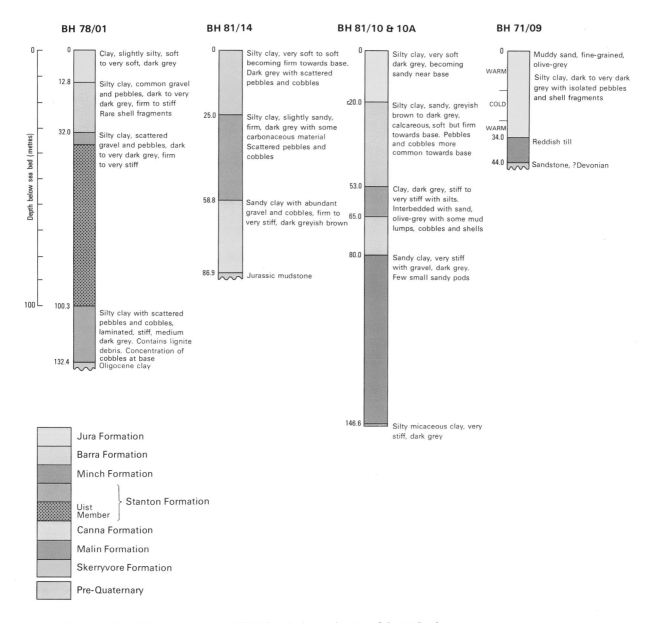

Figure 52 Simplified lithologs of selected BGS boreholes in the Sea of the Hebrides. For locations see Figure 55.

trol is available, Malin B is interpreted as fluvioglacial in origin where it is in intimate contact with Malin A, and possibly as a proglacial, lacustrine deposit in the Blackstones Basin (Davies et al., 1984). The latter interpretation has been doubted by Sutherland (1984) on the grounds of the unit's distribution and depth.

There appears to have been localised downcutting between deposition of the Malin Formation and the overlying Canna Formation (Figure 54); this erosional surface may represent a substantial period of time. The Malin Formation is considered from its areal extent, thickness, and stratigraphical position beneath two major erosive levels (Davies et al., 1984), to have been deposited during a pre-Devensian glaciation.

CANNA FORMATION

Above the Malin Formation is the Canna Formation, a unit commonly only 10 m thick, but which locally reaches 50 m in thickness to the south-west of Canna. It is the oldest formation that crops out in this region (Figure 55), and was deposited disconformably upon the Malin Formation as well as directly upon bedrock (Figures 53 and 54). It is characterised acoustically either by a series of short, discontinuous and ran-

domly spaced reflectors or as a transparent sequence. The type borehole, 81/14, indicates that it comprises firm to very stiff, dark grey to brown, silty, sandy clays with numerous pebbles and cobbles (Figure 52). It is suggested that the Canna Formation is a fairly rapidly deposited glaciomarine sediment that is certainly pre-late Devensian, and perhaps pre-Devensian in age in view of the widespread erosion surface (Figure 54) separating it from younger units (Davies et al., 1984).

STANTON FORMATION

The Stanton Formation is the most readily identifiable seismic unit in the Hebridean region. Its name is derived from the Stanton Banks, around which it reaches thicknesses of over 160 m (Figure 56). The formation lies either upon bedrock or on a widespread erosion surface across the top of the Skerryvore, Malin and Canna formations. It is not found east of 6°40'W, or west of 8°30'W outside the report area. The formation (Stanton A of Davies et al., 1984) is characterised by extremely well-stratified reflectors (Figures 42, 46 and 53) that are commonly draped over irregularities in the rockhead, such as igneous bodies. It also exhibits isolated

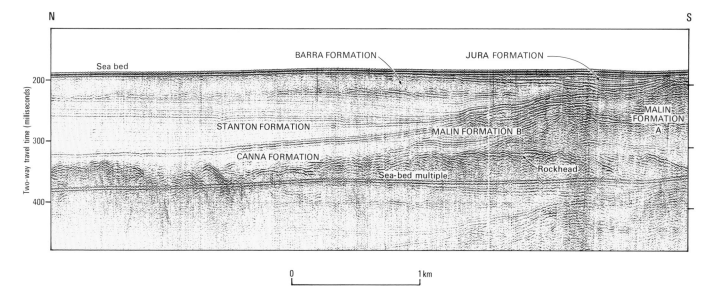

N   S

Figure 53 Sparker profile showing the relationships of Quaternary formations in the Malin Basin. For location see Figure 55. Reproduced courtesy of the Institute of Earth Studies, University College of Wales, Aberystwyth.

point-source diffraction hyperbolae, and probable former pock-marks occur over a small area to the south of the Stanton Banks (Davies et al., 1984). Within the formation, the Uist Member (Stanton B of Davies et al., 1984) appears in many places as an acoustically transparent wedge. However, where the Uist Member reaches its maximum thickness in excess of 90 m, short internal reflectors can be observed on seismic records.

In the type borehole, 78/01 (Figure 52), the lithology of both the Stanton Formation and the Uist Member is dark grey, stiff, laminated silty clay with lignite debris, shell fragments and dropstones. Together with the results of micropalaeontological analysis, this points to sedimentation in a glaciomarine environment, with the Uist Member having been deposited during the severest glacial conditions. Seismic evidence indicates that the Uist Member accumulated far more rapidly than the remainder of the formation, although it cannot be readily distinguished lithologically.

The Stanton Formation underlies a major unconformity (Figures 46 and 54) attributed by Davies et al. (1984) to late Devensian glacial erosion; they therefore thought the Stanton Formation to be of early and/or middle Devensian age. This inference has been confirmed by an amino-acid racemisation result at 100.7 m depth in borehole 78/01, just beneath the Uist Member, on the species *E. excavatum*. This gave a value of 0.087, which in comparison with results from the North Sea, would suggest an early Devensian age.

Davies et al. (1984) suggested that at a time when the Stanton Formation was deposited, grounded glaciers were located for long periods of time over the Scottish mainland and the Inner Hebrides, terminating within the Inner Hebrides (Sissons, 1981). There is no direct chronological control on these sediments, and this model of early to middle Devensian conditions is at variance with Jardine's (1977) proposal, made without sedimentary or dating evidence, that the coastline lay close to the continental margin 40 000 years ago.

The Firth of Clyde region

Within the Firth of Clyde region, a single basal till unit recognised overlying rockhead is generally up to 30 m thick (BGS Clyde Sea Bed Sediments and Quaternary Geology sheet). This basal till has been assumed to be late Devensian

in age (Deegan et al., 1973), although this may not be entirely the case since a few pre-late Devensian deposits have been identified onshore near the coast.

Recent work near Irvine has demonstrated the existence of a pre-late Devensian ice sheet, for organic deposits dated around 30 000 years BP occur between two tills (Jardine et al., 1988). A mammoth's tusk within sands and gravels beneath late-Devensian till has been found at Dreghorn (Craig, 1887). At Kilmaurs, a molar and nine tusks of mammoth and several reindeer antlers were recovered from clay containing freshwater seeds beneath marine deposits that were in turn overlain by till (Young and Craig, 1871). An initial date of 13 700 ± 1500 BP on a tusk from Kilmaurs (Sissons, 1964) has been rejected following a subsequent dating of greater than 40 000 years BP for a reindeer antler from the same site (Shotton et al., 1970).

Other deposits similar to the marine shell beds at Kilmaurs have been found on Kintyre, on the southern coast of Arran, and at Afton Lodge in Ayrshire (Figure 47; Sutherland, 1981a). Where in situ, these undated sediments suggest deposition at a time when the land was isostatically depressed or global sea levels were high. The former explanation is preferred, and may have been either before the late Devensian, or immediately following the late Devensian glacial maximum (A G Dawson, oral communication, 1990).

LATE DEVENSIAN

About 25 000 years ago, during the late Devensian, the onset of global cooling brought glacial conditions to the report area as the North Atlantic Polar Front, presently found well north of Iceland, moved southwards to reach the Iberian Peninsula 18 000 years ago (CLIMAP, 1976). A large ice sheet developed over the Highlands of Scotland and spread outwards; similar but smaller ice sheets developed in the upland areas of Skye, Mull and Arran, only to be incorporated into the expanding mainland ice cap (Sutherland, 1984). A separate ice cap in the Outer Hebrides appears to have behaved independently of the mainland ice cap (Sutherland, 1984). The eastern coast of the Outer Hebrides shows indications of eastward ice movement (Peacock, 1984), and there is much evidence on the Scottish mainland and the Inner Hebrides of

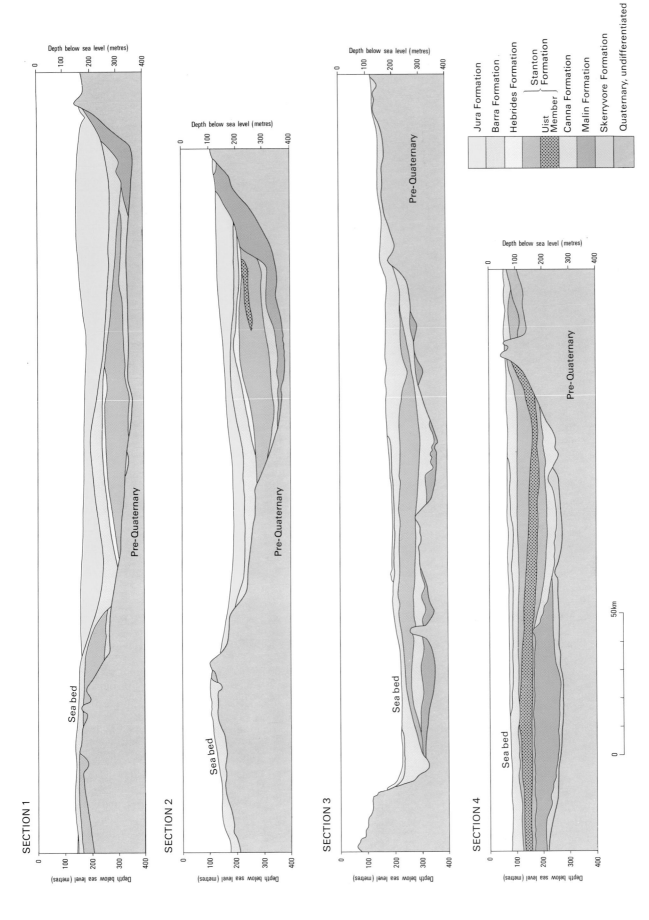

Figure 54 Cross-sections showing the relationships of Quaternary formations in the Sea of the Hebrides. For locations see Figure 55.

65

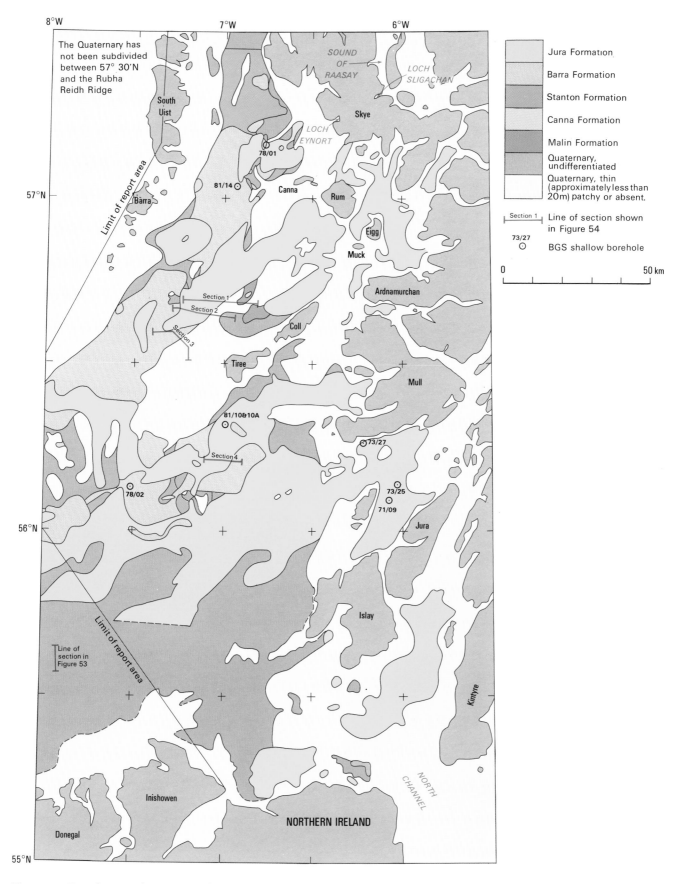

Figure 55 Distribution of Quaternary formations to the south of Skye.

66

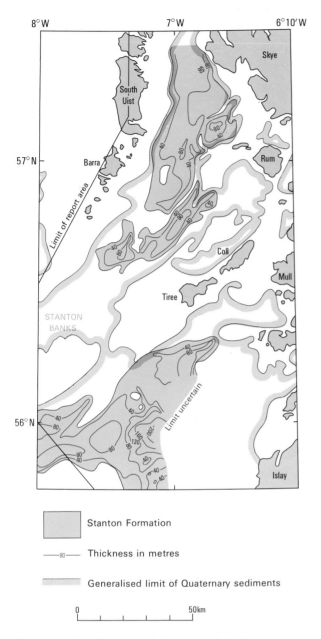

Figure 56 Distribution and thickness of the Stanton Formation.

westward ice movement. It is likely that the two ice sheets co-alesced at the glacial maximum of 18 000 years ago.

As on the surrounding land, the products of the late Devensian glaciation are the major component of Quaternary deposits offshore in the report area. The marine record, as inter-preted by Davies et al. (1984), shows that the mainland ice sheet merged with, and was deflected south-westwards by, the south-ern part of the Outer Hebrides ice sheet and extended out to the shelf edge west of the report area (Figure 57). The submarine to-pography is also likely to have encouraged the ice sheet to move in that direction. However, unlike an earlier glaciation that de-posited the extensive and thick till of the Malin Formation, the late Devensian glaciation of the Hebridean region produced a widespread, low-relief regional erosion surface that is only patchily covered by a thin diamicton.

In The Minch, Bishop and Jones (1979) and Chesher et al. (1983) identified a large arcuate morainic ridge, some 60 km in length, termed the Greenstone Ridge (Figures 49 and 57). Although these authors suggested that it is a medial moraine, its size led Sutherland (1984) to suggest that it is the end moraine of the last, late Devensian, glaciation. Readvance

moraines in Northern Ireland (the Drumlin Readvance and the Armoy Readvance) have been linked to the central Islay moraine, which is possibly dated between 14 000 and 15 000 years ago (Stephens and McCabe, 1977).

Although global sea level fell by more than 100 m (Fairbanks, 1989) due to the volume of water held within the very large late Devensian ice sheets around the world, isostat-ic loading depressed the land until relative sea level rose above that of the present day. For example, in Islay the sea level reached about 25 m above OD, compared with higher than 70 m above OD during the early Devensian (Dawson, 1988). Highest marine levels were reached closest to the ice sheet centre at Rannoch Moor (Figure 57); levels of 35 m to 40 m above OD were experienced at Loch Long and Loch Fyne (Gray and Sutherland, 1977; Sutherland, 1981b). West-wards, sea level at the late Devensian ice-sheet maximum was lower; Stephens and Synge (1965) reported a possibly equiv-alent sea level of 20 to 23 m in Donegal.

Late Devensian glaciomarine deposits have consequently been recorded at several coastal sites, and can be compared

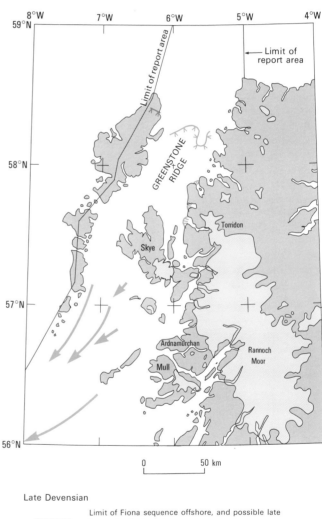

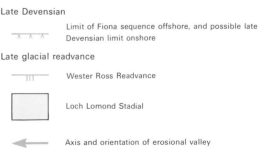

Figure 57 Late Devensian and younger ice limits. After BGS maps, Davies et al. (1984), Sutherland (1984), and Ballantyne et al. (1991).

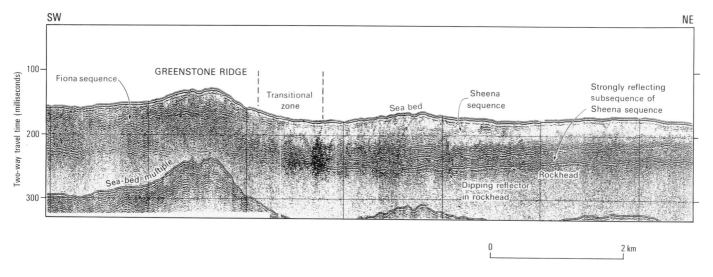

Figure 58 Annotated sparker profile showing the lateral transition between the Fiona and Sheena sequences. For location see Figure 49.

with those offshore. Deposits at Kilchiaran in western Islay (Figure 47) predate a late Devensian end-moraine complex in central Islay that is possibly the result of a readvance, and may be equivalent to the Barra Formation (Figure 48) offshore (Benn and Dawson, 1987). It comprises a diamicton, with rare arctic fossils, believed to have been deposited in close proximity to the glacial margin. Similar deposits on the Rhinns of Islay and The Oa (Figure 47), up to a height of 80 m above OD (Dawson, 1988), may belong to an earlier, more extensive marine transgression. Their existence and the absence of till overlying them imply that such areas of the Hebrides may not have been glaciated during the late Devensian.

At Lochgilphead (Figure 47), fossiliferous, late-glacial, marine sediments (Crosskey and Robertson, 1871) above a basal till are dated between about 12 500 and 11 000 years BP, and represent the Windermere Interstadial (Peacock et al., 1977). These deposits have been correlated with the Clyde Beds around Glasgow, and may also partly equate with the Jura Formation (Figure 48) offshore.

During the Loch Lomond Stadial from 11 000 to 10 000 years ago, there was significant glacial cover of north-west Scotland, Skye and Mull (Figure 57). There are a few coastal occurrences of glaciomarine deposits dating from the Loch Lomond Stadial (Peacock et al., 1989), some of which have been reworked by ice of the Loch Lomond Readvance. A notable feature associated with these deposits is the Main Rock Platform, formed as the shoreline was subjected to severe periglacial conditions, perhaps as a trimming of a pre-existing rock platform (Dawson, 1980; 1988). In the Sound of Raasay (Figure 55), there is evidence that glaciers reached present-day sea level at Loch Sligachan and Loch Eynort (Walker et al., 1988; Ballantyne et al., 1991), as well as in sea lochs on the west coast of mainland Scotland between Torridon and Ardnamurchan (Figure 57).

The Minch region

MORAG SEQUENCE

The Morag sequence is the oldest late Devensian seismic unit identified in The Minch, where it is widely distributed overlying an erosion surface at the top of the Jean and Aisla sequences (Figures 50 and 51). From comparison with the Hebridean region, this erosion surface may represent the ad-

vance of late Devensian ice prior to the retreat of the ice front into The Minch. The Morag sequence is seismically well bedded, with generally regular internal reflectors that tend to drape the underlying topography (Figure 51). The sequence is typically 25 to 30 m thick, but is locally up to 50 m thick. In borehole 76/55 (Figure 49), the unit comprises soft to firm, silty clay with few pebbles, and is of typical glaciomarine aspect; the dinoflagellate-cyst assemblage indicates deposition in a cold, nearshore, marine environment (BGS Lewis Quaternary Geology; Sutherland Sea Bed Sediments and Quaternary Geology sheets). These sediments were probably deposited beyond the ice front during or soon after the late Devensian glacial maximum.

FIONA SEQUENCE

The Fiona sequence crops out south of about 58°15'N (Figure 49), where it is seismically a largely dense, structureless, hummocky deposit with locally persistent internal reflectors (Figure 58). It exhibits positive relief, is up to 90 m thick, and grades laterally northwards and eastwards into both the Morag and Sheena sequences. The eastern limit of the Fiona sequence forms the Greenstone Ridge, and although no samples have been recovered from it, it is considered to be morainic, perhaps comprising subglacial or proglacial sediments deposited by the late Devensian ice sheet (BGS Sutherland Sea Bed Sediments and Quaternary Geology sheet).

If the marked erosion surface beneath the Fiona and Morag sequences represents the late Devensian glacial advance (BGS Lewis Quaternary Geology sheet), then the Fiona–Morag boundary cannot represent the late Devensian ice limit, for the erosion surface extends at least 40 km to the north-north-west of the Butt of Lewis. The only major readvance in this northern area after the late Devensian maximum was the relatively limited Wester Ross Readvance at 13 500 to 13 000 years BP (Robinson and Ballantyne, 1979; Ballantyne and Sutherland, 1987). Its limit on Skye and the Scottish mainland was close to the ice centres, extending no farther than the mouths of sea lochs (Figure 57), some distance from the limit of the Fiona sequence. On this basis, the northernmost extent of the Fiona sequence (Figure 49) could be taken to represent the former extent of the late Devensian ice sheet (Figure 57), a concept which fits well with theoretical calculations based on maximum altitudes of that ice sheet on the Trotternish Peninsula (Ballantyne, 1990). The erosion surface beneath the Morag sequence may therefore be the result of one or more earlier ice advances.

SHEENA SEQUENCE

This is typically a seismically structureless to transparent unit with diffraction hyperbolae (Figure 51). In the south it grades laterally into the Fiona sequence. It does not extend as far north as the underlying Morag sequence (Figure 49), and in the south-east includes a lower, strongly reflecting, bedded subsequence (Figure 58). In borehole 76/55 (Figure 49) it forms a dark to very dark grey, soft, pebbly, silty clay of glaciomarine character. Micropalaeontological analysis of the stiffer, less pebbly, and more marginal undifferentiated unit in nearby borehole 72/32 suggests deposition in a severe, cold, nearshore, less than fully marine environment; this unit may be laterally equivalent to the Sheena sequence. It is thought that the Sheena sequence was deposited in a marine embayment in The Minch, farther offshore than the sediment in borehole 72/32 and perhaps immediately north of the contemporary late Devensian ice sheet (Figure 57) which deposited the Fiona sequence (BGS Sutherland Sea Bed Sediments and Quaternary Geology sheet).

ANNIE SEQUENCE

The Annie sequence is a clearly differentiated unit near the top of the Minch supersequence (Figure 48), that normally displays very fine seismic lamination. It unconformably infills hollows (Figures 16 and 50) and displays internal reflectors which drape the underlying topography. It rarely exceeds 25 m in thickness, although it fills a rockhead basin to a thickness of 90 m south-east of Stornoway, where gas blanking is also recorded. In BGS borehole 78/04, drilled into this basin (Figure 49), detailed palaeontological and chronostratigraphical analyses have shown that the sequence represents the time from the withdrawal of late Devensian ice to the Holocene (Graham et al., 1990). Included within the sequence is clear evidence for the cold climate associated with the Loch Lomond Stadial. This is confirmed by radiocarbon dates both above and below the cold interval in the core, and by the presence within the cold interval of tephra geochemically equated with the 10 600 year old Vedde Ash Bed.

There are considerable similarities between the Annie sequence and the Jura Formation to the south, as well as with other late-glacial, acoustically well-layered, soft to very soft, clay-dominated sediments elsewhere around the UK, including the Witch Ground Formation in the central North Sea (Stoker et al., 1985). These sediments all exhibit the transition from arctic to interstadial conditions, followed by the cold interval of the Loch Lomond Stadial and subsequent amelioration to Holocene temperate conditions. In the Sound of Raasay, there is evidence that during the Loch Lomond Stadial, glaciers locally reached the sea (Walker et al., 1988) (Figure 57).

CATRIONA SEQUENCE

The Catriona sequence occurs at the sea bed in four outliers (Figure 49), where it is seismically well bedded to transparent (Figure 51), locally with a prograding character. It is up to 40 m thick off the Butt of Lewis, but only reaches 20 m thickness elsewhere. It forms positive topographic relief on the sea floor (Figures 50 and 51), rather than occurring in hollows as is characteristic of the Annie sequence. The base of the unit is clear and is locally irregular, perhaps indicative of iceberg ploughing (Figure 51). In borehole 72/33 (Figure 49) it comprises a slightly muddy, fine-grained, grey sand with shell fragments, and is of marine origin. The Catriona sequence is

either younger than, or contemporaneous with, the Annie sequence (Figure 48), and represents deposition during latest Devensian or early Flandrian times in a higher-energy, shallower environment, possibly as sandbanks.

The Hebridean region

HEBRIDES AND MINCH FORMATIONS

South of Skye, the seismostratigraphical studies of Davies et al. (1984) indicate a major erosion surface truncating the Stanton and older formations, or grading on to rockhead (Figure 54). This unconformity is overlain by a thin, unsampled layer up to 20 m thick, with hyperbolic reflections that are suggestive of boulders. In the main depositional basins, the erosion surface is relatively smooth, with wide, open valleys tens of kilometres in length. These valleys are north-easterly orientated, turning to an east-north-easterly alignment at the western edge of the report area. Both the morphology and areal extent of the erosion surface preclude an origin by either fluvial processes or marine erosion. Glacial erosion, probably during the late Devensian, appears to be the only plausible origin for such a feature; the topography of the erosion surface suggests that mainland ice moved south-westwards beyond the report area towards the shelfbreak.

The thin remnants of till left by the glaciation are termed the Hebrides Formation. Davies et al. (1984) suggested that the Hebrides Formation may be correlated with the Minch Formation recognised by Boulton et al. (1981) between Skye and Ardnamurchan (Figure 48). The Minch Formation is a till that lies beneath glaciomarine sediments, but it is not stratigraphically constrained, and may include material older than late Devensian. The Minch Formation has been mapped from seismic profiles between Mull and Jura, and was sampled in three BGS boreholes (71/09, 73/25 and 73/27) as a coarse-grained diamicton of variable colour, and up to 10 m thick (Figure 55; BGS Tiree Quaternary Geology sheet).

BARRA FORMATION

This formation overlies earlier Quaternary formations, as well as pre-Quaternary rocks, and has a maximum thickness of about 130 m in the western part of the Sea of the Hebrides. Over large areas, the formation has low internal seismic reflectivity, recording as almost acoustically transparent (Figure 42); its seismic signature is similar to that of the Canna Formation, implying high rates of accumulation to Davies et al. (1984). Micropalaeontological analyses of silty clays with dropstones from borehole 78/02 (Figure 55) suggest a complex glaciomarine origin (Davies et al., 1984). It is thought that the Barra Formation was deposited under stadial conditions immediately following the late Devensian glacial maximum, when sea levels were rising quickly over an isostatically depressed surface. Some of the shorelines and glaciomarine deposits on Islay may correlate with this interval (Benn and Dawson, 1987; Dawson, 1988).

JURA FORMATION

The Jura Formation comprises sediments that are generally acoustically well layered (Figure 53), and commonly fill deep hollows in either rockhead or Quaternary deposits. The formation tends to be thickest close to the Inner Hebrides, where it locally exceeds 300 m. At the sea bed in the Sound of Jura, there has been extensive erosion, by tidal scour, of closed channels up to 80 m deep into the Jura Formation (Evans and Ruckley, 1980).

The sediments typically comprise very soft to firm, dark grey, silty clays with isolated pebbles and shell fragments. Micropalaeontological analyses of the type borehole, 71/09

(Figure 52), show that both cold and warm faunas are represented, suggesting fluctuating conditions which have been interpreted as representing the warm–cold–warm pattern of the late Devensian to Holocene climate (Binns et al., 1974a; Robinson, 1980). A date of $16\,470 \pm 300$ years BP obtained from the base of the Jura Formation in borehole 71/09 could be taken to suggest rapid retreat of the ice front since the glacial maximum at about 18 000 years. However, it has been suggested that some dead carbon was included in the dated sample (Binns in Harkness and Wilson, 1974), and Davies et al. (1984) proposed that the base of the formation is some 13 500 years old. It would therefore date from the time when the Polar Front was migrating northwards across the area, and polar waters were retreating northwards from the vicinity of the British Isles (Ruddiman et al., 1977). The unit partly correlates with the Clyde Beds onshore (Peacock, 1981), and equates lithologically, and probably temporally, with the Annie sequence of The Minch (Figure 48).

Towards the east, there is a tendency to intraformational erosion, and acoustic blanking due to gas (BGS Tiree Quaternary Geology sheet; Figure 39). In the Inner Hebrides, between the island of Eigg and the mainland (Figure 55) and within several sounds, acoustic turbidity and 'gas domes' were located by Boulton et al. (1981) where the Jura Formation sediment attains a thickness of 10 to 30 m. The sediments are associated with very high rates of deposition from suspension in a marine environment, and the areas of doming could be ascribed to prolonged elevated pore pressures caused by trapped gases (Hovland and Judd, 1988). Boulton et al. (1981, p 50) concluded that 'it seems likely that the gas production is related to a relatively high content of organic material, possibly much of it vegetable matter washed in from the nearby land areas'.

In the approaches to the Firth of Lorne, a boulder layer or pavement identified by a series of overlapping point source diffractions near the top of the formation prevents acoustic penetration (BGS Tiree Quaternary Geology sheet). This layer may represent marine sedimentation of dropstones from icebergs during the Loch Lomond Stadial (Davies et al., 1984), when an ice cap was developed over much of the western Highlands (Figure 57). Sediments ascribed to the Loch Lomond Stadial have been identified from a zone of cold fauna reported by Binns et al. (1974a) between 16 and 26 m depth in borehole 71/09 (Figure 52).

The Firth of Clyde region

No stratigraphy has yet been established for Quaternary deposits in the Firth of Clyde region. They have however been interpreted as late Devensian to Flandrian in age (Deegan et al., 1973), although parts of the succession may be older. Interpretation of sparker records and borehole material indicates the presence of a basal diamicton layer up to 30 m thick, generally comprising stiff, reddish brown to greyish brown clay with sand, pebbles or cobbles. This basal diamicton thickens to become the predominant Quaternary deposit to the east of Great Cumbrae (Figure 47), in parts of Loch Fyne where it is 110 m thick, and immediately east of Campbeltown. (BGS Clyde Sea Bed Sediments and Quaternary Geology sheet).

Overlying the till is an acoustically well-layered or transparent unit whose internal reflectors are generally horizontal or subhorizontal. This unit is very variable in thickness, and is over 160 m thick north-east of Arran. The unit comprises grey to brown, soft, calcareous, silty clay, commonly with organic material. It is locally pink at the base, and may also contain sparse shell fragments (Deegan et al., 1973). The clays are considered to be marine deposits of late-glacial age that may in part correlate with the Clyde Beds (BGS Clyde Sea Bed Sediments and Quaternary Geology sheet), which were deposited during a time of marine inundation prior to isostatic uplift of the recently deglaciated land (Peacock, 1981). However, dinoflagellate-cyst analyses of offshore sequences suggest a warm–cold–warm climatic succession associated respectively with postglacial warming, the Loch Lomond Stadial, and subsequent amelioration (Harland in Deegan et al., 1973). This sequence therefore represents a much longer interval than that of the Clyde Beds alone, and the base of these clays offshore may well be older than the Clyde Beds onshore, for the ice retreated and the sea entered the Firth of Clyde earlier than it did, temporarily, around Glasgow. In the thicker basins there may also be an appreciable component of Holocene sediments in the sequence.

HOLOCENE

The climatic warming after the Loch Lomond Stadial resulted in a rise in global sea level which continued until about 6000 years ago. Within the report area, this rise was overtaken about 6500 years ago by isostatic uplift of the mainland, which continues today at a rate of 1.8 mm/year to the north of Great Cumbrae (Shennan, 1989), and may exceed 2 mm/year in the centre of uplift at Rannoch Moor (I Shennan, oral communication, 1990). Uplift is reduced farther away from the centre of isostatic depression, and is presently negative in the Outer Hebrides (Peacock, 1984). However, an anomalous uplift of 2.4 mm/year has been reported for Malin Head (Carter et al., 1989).

The acoustically well-layered units of the Annie and Catriona sequences, the Jura Formation, and the unnamed successions in the Firth of Clyde, all extend into the Holocene. In borehole 78/04 (Figure 49), Holocene strata are some 15 m thick (Graham et al., 1990), and there is a similar thickness in borehole 71/09 (Figure 52). The dating of both boreholes suggest that the Holocene sediments were deposited early in this interval.

11 Sea-bed sediments

The sediment distribution pattern within the Malin–Hebrides sea area shows a great variety of sediment types and rapid lateral changes of grain size. These characteristics are the products of uneven sediment supply, the extremely variable water depth, and a diversity of tidal-current conditions. The very limited sediment transport into the area is largely restricted to fluvial input, most notably from the River Clyde. The only other significant input is bioclastic debris, much of which is swept into the area around the Butt of Lewis and along the northern coast of Ireland. The sediment is largely derived from reworking of the underlying Pleistocene deposits, particularly during the Holocene transgression.

The sea-bed topography of the report area is by far the most variable of any area on the UK shelf (Figure 2; Pantin, 1991). There is relatively shallow water adjacent to the coastline and over many submerged banks and craggy ridges, but there are several enclosed deeps that descend to over 200 m depth. In two areas, water depths exceed 300 m. This physiographic diversity is due to glacial erosion acting on rocks of greatly variable strengths; the deeps tend to be formed over Mesozoic sediments, whereas areas intruded by igneous rocks, or formed of basement, normally occur as ridges. The large areas of deep water mainly have a north-westerly orientation as a consequence of the regional geological structure, which was exploited by ice to overdeepen the basinal areas.

Tidal currents in the area are very variable. In the north, sea-surface maximum tidal current velocities (Figure 59) are generally less than 0.5 m/s in unrestricted waters, although velocities of up to 5 m/s occur in the Inner Sound (Bishop and Jones, 1979). Current velocities of about 1 m/s are experienced between Rubha Reidh and Cape Wrath, more than 1 m/s between Rubha Hunish and north Harris, and over 2 m/s north-west of the Shiant Islands. Velocities up to 2.5 m/s also occur around the Butt of Lewis (Bishop and Jones, 1979). Manned submersible observations in the Inner Sound and Sound of Sleat indicate restricted visibility due to the quantity of sediment moved at the sea bed by strong currents (Eden et al., 1971).

In the Malin Sea, maximum tidal currents frequently reach up to 1.5 m/s between Islay and the north Irish coast, and exceed 2 m/s around Rathlin Island (Sager and Sammler, 1975). Within the North Channel, surface tidal currents are over 2.3 m/s, with predicted mean peak bottom currents greater than 1.5 m/s; such currents are sufficient to erode and transport loose sediment of sand grade, and affect both the sediment and bedform types (see Figure 61). There are also strong tidal currents between some islands, notably in the Gulf of Corryvreckan between Jura and Scarba where the spring rate of the west-going stream reaches over 4.0 m/s (BGS Tiree Sea Bed Sediment sheet).

Mapping of sea-bed sediments has been largely dependent on BGS sampling employing a Shipek grab, which collects material from approximately the top 5 cm of sediment. The results of this work are published as a series of 1:250 000 maps (see inside back cover), which have been simplified to construct Figure 60, which uses a classification scheme modified from Folk (1954). The distribution of rock outcrop has been determined using seismic-reflection and sidescan sonar equipment; the latter commonly indicates a patchy cover of sediment lying on outcrop.

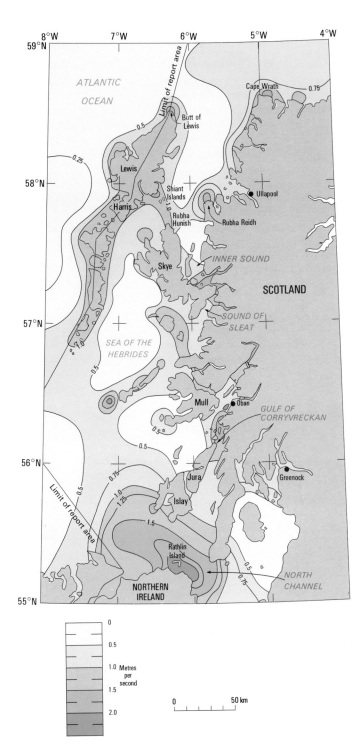

Figure 59 Surface tidal-stream velocities at spring tides. After Sager and Sammler (1975).

Sediment thickness upon Quaternary deposits or older rocks is extremely variable, ranging from less than 10 cm in some areas of gravel and lithic sands to more than 10 m in carbonate-rich sand waves. Large, composite sand waves occur on sandbanks in the Malin Sea; the maximum recorded thickness is 30 m on Hempton's Turbot Bank

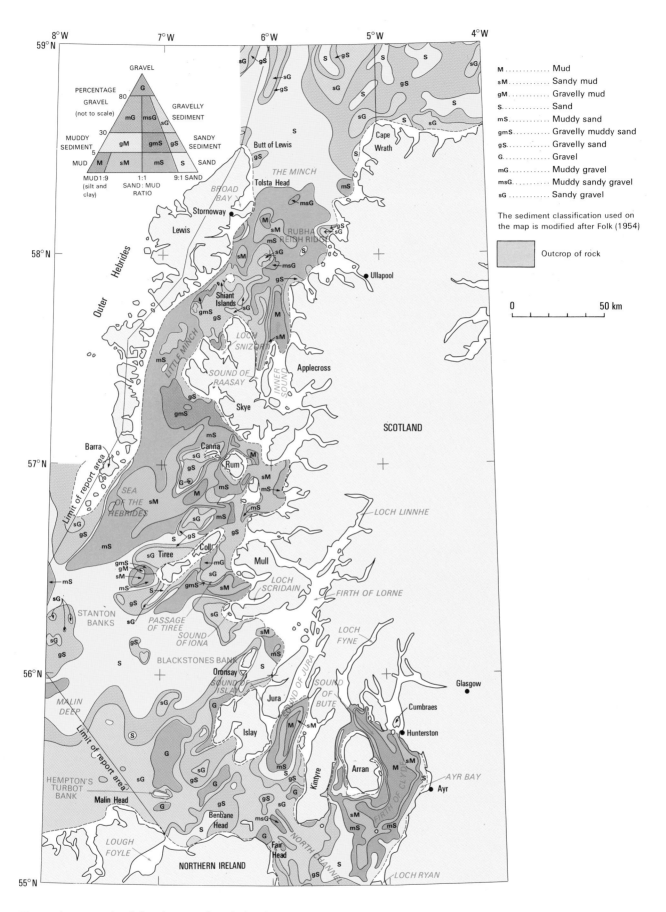

Figure 60 Generalised distribution of sea-bed sediments in the Malin–Hebrides area.

(Pendlebury and Dobson, 1976) (Figure 60). In some areas of mud, the sea-bed sediments are indistinguishable from the underlying late- to postglacial clay, in which the Holocene deposits can be 10 m or more in thickness.

SEDIMENT DISTRIBUTION

Figure 60 is a very generalised representation of a surface-sediment distribution which may show abrupt changes in particle size (Eden et al., 1971; 1973). In this account, the sediments are subdivided into three groups: gravelly sediments, sandy sediments and muddy sediments. There are also localities where rock outcrop is predominant.

Gravelly sediments

Gravelly sediments are here taken as those with more than 30 per cent gravel (Figure 60). In the Little Minch and The Minch they are distributed in shallow-water areas, in particular around the Shiant Islands and off many headlands such as north and north-west of Cape Wrath. No significant gravel deposits are found in water deeper than 100 m.

The gravels in the north contain varying amounts of lithic and biogenic material; an examination of rock types within the lithic gravel component (Bishop and Jones, 1979) revealed that Mesozoic clasts are restricted to zones off Skye and Raasay, although there are other minor occurrences off Applecross and on the southern edge of the Rubha Reidh Ridge. Igneous clasts, largely basalts and gabbros, have a similar distribution but extend over a wider area to cover both flanks of the Rubha Reidh Ridge. The distribution of Lewisian and Torridonian clasts reflects their onshore outcrop; the gravels off the Outer Hebrides have clast assemblages that are totally of Lewisian origin, whereas on the eastern side of The Minch the clasts are more varied, and their distribution suggests some north-westerly lineation that may imply glacial movement away from the mainland (Bishop and Jones, 1979).

The biogenic component of the gravel fraction in The Minch is dominated by the skeletal remains of recent organisms (Bishop and Jones, 1979). Bivalves predominate, but a wide range of gastropods make up a small proportion of the assemblage. Other biogenic materials include scaphopods in the northern Minch, and small solitary corals at the southern end of the Little Minch. Close to areas of rock outcrop, the biogenic gravel includes *Balanus* and echinoderms. In gravels with significant amounts of mud, biogenic gravel is either absent or restricted to *Pecten* and *Turritella*.

In the Sea of the Hebrides (Figure 60), gravels are found on, or adjacent to, rock platforms such as the Stanton Banks and Blackstones Bank, as well as off south-west Mull, Tiree, Coll and Canna. The gravels on sea-bed highs may be intermittently distributed and less than 10 cm thick, but can be thicker around the coast, particularly off headlands with strong currents. In areas where a rocky substrate is subject to severe wave action, such as in the Sound of Iona and off Ardnamurchan (Figure 60), barnacles constitute the major part of the biogenic component (Farrow et al., 1978). There are many submerged rock cliffs within the Hebridean region; these commonly have angular, coarse, scree deposits at their bases (Eden et al., 1971). Scree-like deposits are not being formed under present conditions, and are inferred to be either of glacial origin or were formed during periods of reduced sea level.

In some areas, muddy gravels are thought to represent a winnowed lag deposit derived from underlying glacial materi-

al. Elsewhere, possibly morainic deposits are being covered with mud at several localities in the Sea of the Hebrides and The Minch. Observations from a submersible have demonstrated the slow deposition of silty, shelly mud on flats and in depressions. This gradual submerging of the morainic debris (Eden et al., 1971; 1973) may explain the local intermixing of gravel and muddy sediments.

The sea-bed sediments in the southern part of the Malin Sea are predominantly gravelly due to the strong currents, and the sediments here tend to have a high carbonate content. The North Channel between Northern Ireland and the Kintyre Peninsula is largely floored by bare rock due to the very strong currents, but where sediments occur, they are invariably gravel dominated (Pantin, 1991). Dobson and Haynes (1973) observed shell-gravel pavements at the southern boundary of the report area.

Sandy sediments

Sandy sediments are those with less than 30 per cent gravel, and have more sand than mud. The sea floor of The Minch and Little Minch is predominantly covered by such sediments (Figure 60), largely muddy sand and gravelly sand. In the very northern part of the report area, well-sorted sand is widespread in the more open waters north of Tolsta Head. Bishop and Jones (1979) show a general improvement in sediment sorting northwards, from extremely poorly sorted sediments off Skye, to extremely well-sorted deposits north of a line from the Butt of Lewis to Cape Wrath.

The well-sorted, predominantly lithic, sands are less than 10 cm thick. They are probably derived from underlying periglacial deposits, having been slightly resorted and deprived of the finer fractions towards the sea bed (Bishop and Jones, 1979). Where the sands are predominantly carbonate, most notably off the coast of Lewis, they tend to be much thicker, in excess of 2 m.

Biogenic sands are primarily composed of shell fragments, mainly those of bivalves, gastropods and echinoderms. Foraminiferal tests constitute less than 5 per cent of the biogenic fraction in The Minch, but this proportion increases towards more open-marine areas (Edwards, 1982). The most significant localities with biogenic sands are the carbonate sandbanks at the northern end of The Minch, where the size range and degree of abrasion suggest that these shell sands are being produced locally (Chesher et al., 1983). However, coastal shell sands on Lewis, and carbonates at the very northern end of the report area, appear to have been transported from the continental shelf west of the Outer Hebrides (Bishop and Jones, 1979). The large north-easterly facing beach at Traigh Mhor to the north of Tolsta Head is formed of shell sand derived from offshore (Steers, 1973). South of Tolsta Head, there are indications that beach sands are being swept out to sea to feed the Melbost Spit at the southern end of Broad Bay (Ritchie and Mather, 1970).

Within the Malin Sea and the Sea of the Hebrides, sandy sediments occur to the north and south of a widespread sand deposit surrounding the Blackstones Bank (Figure 60). To the north, in the deeper waters at the southern end of the Sea of the Hebrides, the sandy sediments are predominantly muddy sands. In the Little Minch, the sea bed comprises muddy sands that are largely gravelly and probably derived from the reworking of glacial sediments. To the south of the Blackstones Bank, the sands become slightly gravelly with increasing bottom currents and are displaced by gravelly sediment, although muddy sand is found in the Malin Deep in water exceeding 160 m in depth. Similarly, tidal currents that increase in strength both to the north and south cause the muddy sediments of the southern part of the Sound of Jura to become increasingly sandier southwards, and to become gravelly towards the north (BGS Clyde Sea Bed Sediments and Quaternary Geology sheet).

In the Malin Sea and the Sea of the Hebrides, sand is mainly restricted to the area between 55° 50'N and 56° 20'N, but is also found near the coasts, especially off Ireland and Islay. The sand between the mouth of Lough Foyle and Benbane Head contains about 35 per cent biogenic material, and has been built up into symmetrical and asymmetrical sand waves up to 18 m high (Pendlebury and Dobson, 1976). Greater biogenic concentrations, of the order of 55 per cent, are recorded in the small zone of sand to the southeast of Islay, where much of the carbonate is composed of the calcareous secreting algae *Lithophyllum* spp. and *Lithothamnium* spp. (Pendelbury and Dobson, 1976).

Within the Firth of Clyde, sands and sandy sediments are largely restricted to the zone within 5 or 10 km of the coast, where water depths are less than 60 m. Sands are dominant in Ayr Bay and southwards to the mouth of Loch Ryan, but also extend south-westwards to the edges of the North Channel where currents of some 1 m/s permit their accumulation. Many of the sediment waves at the eastern margin of the North Channel comprise sand (BGS Clyde Sea Bed Sediments and Quaternary Geology sheet).

Muddy sediments

Muddy sediments are those which have less than 30 per cent gravel, and include more mud than sand (Figure 60). They occur both in relatively deep-water areas and in the more sheltered locations of lesser depth. Their distributions locally correlate with that of acoustically well-layered, late- and postglacial clays such as the Jura Formation and Annie sequence.

In The Minch, muddy sediments occur particularly in deep-water locations off Stornoway, in the Sound of Raasay and in the Inner Sound. They are also found in an indistinct basin in the central part of The Minch, and in some sheltered lochs and bays (Figure 60). Muds occupy the central, deepest parts of these basins, normally where the water depths exceed 120 m. A manned submersible dive into the Inner Sound revealed mud adhering to rock ledges, and even to very steep rock faces (Eden et al., 1971); here the mud is greyish brown and contains a small amount of shell debris. The thickest surface sediments occur in the mud-floored depressions of the Inner Sound, Sound of Raasay, Loch Snizort and off Stornoway, where the present-day sea-bed material is indistinguishable from the underlying late-glacial to Holocene sediments. Measurements of clay mineral assemblages (Bishop and Jones, 1979) suggest that modern muds in The Minch and Little Minch are derived from reworking of Quaternary tills and glaciomarine deposits, with only a minor input from the adjacent land.

In the 'open-sea' regions of the Sea of the Hebrides, muddy sediments form an extensive zone north of 56° 40'N (Figure 60), usually where water depths exceed 100 m. Only in the central part of this muddy zone and in the sea lochs are true muds found. Muddy sediments have also been mapped off the western side of Mull, in the Firth of Lorne, and in a small area west of Tiree, and are found in sea lochs such as Loch Linnhe and Loch Scridain. As is the case farther north, sea-bed boulders to the east of Barra have been observed to be mantled with muddy sediment (Dobson and Haynes, 1973).The only muddy sediments in the Malin Sea occur where they overlie thick Jura Formation sediments at the southern end of the Sound of Jura.

Muddy sediments are widely distributed within the Firth of Clyde, usually where the water is between 60 and 80 m deep. These sediments floor much of Kilbrannan Sound (Figure 2), the area around the Cumbraes, and the southern part of the firth. Mud occupies all the deeper-water areas of the Firth of Clyde (Figure 60) where tidal currents are less than 0.5 m/s, and is most extensively developed east and south of Arran and at the southern end of Kilbrannan Sound.

The sea-floor sediments of the central deeps of the sea lochs are also predominantly muddy; detailed observations from a submersible in lower Loch Fyne revealed that the muds occupy a central channel less than 0.5 km wide between rock walls up to 80 m high (Eden et al., 1971). Manganese nodules are exposed on the sea floor, and are also believed to be buried just below the surface (Eden et al., 1971). These nodules have been sampled in many sea lochs around the Firth of Clyde (Deegan et al., 1973).

Farrow and Fyfe (1988) show occurrences of mud with generally more than 10 per cent carbonate in the Firth of Clyde, the Sea of the Hebrides and The Minch, exceeding 20 per cent only locally. The carbonate in the mud is generally low-Mg calcite derived from abrasion of barnacles and algal grazing of shells (Farrow et al., 1978). In mud-dominated areas of The Minch with low rates of sedimentation, foraminifera constitute the major calcareous component of the sediments (Edwards, 1982).

Rock outcrop

In many parts of the report area there is little or no loose sediment on the sea floor, so that large areas of rock platform are exposed due either to their positive topographic form or to strong bottom currents preventing the deposition of sediment. The principal areas of rock outcrop are the North Channel, Stanton Banks, Blackstones Bank, Hawes Bank (Figure 2) and the rock platforms which extend westwards from Canna, Tiree, south-west Mull and Islay (Figure 47). Submersible observations reveal that these rock platforms include many gullies, which trap sediment mainly consisting of biogenic, coarse-grained sand (Eden et al., 1971; 1973). The North Channel is the most significant zone of low-lying rock outcrop (Caston, 1975; 1976); any glacial deposits here have been removed, and all superficial deposits are mobile. Due to differential erosion, Tertiary dykes (Figures 44 and 45) stand up to 28 m above the base of adjacent eroded hollows in the Permo-Triassic country rock (Caston, 1975).

BEDFORMS

Close to the north-eastern coast of Lewis, in zones of shell-rich sand, Bishop (1977) identified both linear and irregular patches on sidescan sonar records; they were attributed to bedforms such as sand waves. Poorly defined patches recorded on sidescan sonar records in the centre of The Minch, and restricted to pre-Annie sequence deposits, may be attributed to iceberg and/or sea-ice keel ploughing of the sea bed. In the southern part of the report area, Banner and Culver (1979) described a simple distribution of sedimentary bedforms that broadly reflects the strength of tidal currents. Sand waves, which are transverse to the tidal current, predominate throughout the Malin Sea, the Inner Hebrides south of Mull, and in the Firth of Clyde. Sand ribbons typical of a higher-energy environment are significant longitudinal sea-bed features between Islay and Malin Head (Pendlebury and Dobson, 1976), as well as in the North Channel (BGS Clyde Sea Bed Sediments and Quaternary sheet).

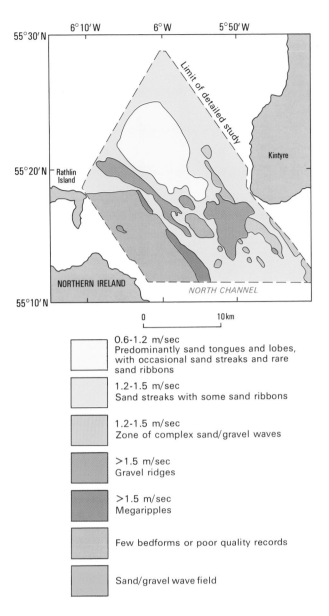

Figure 61 Bedform distribution and estimated mean-spring, near-surface tidal currents in part of the North Channel. See Figure 44 for location of the area covered by diagram.

In the lower-energy parts of the Sea of the Hebrides, sand ripples have been observed in gullies between rock outcrops on the Stanton Banks (Eden et al., 1973); the ripples are symmetrical, 100 to 250 mm high, with wavelengths of 0.75 to 1.5 m. They comprise whitish shell sand, usually of coarse-sand size, and have a wide range of orientations, but most commonly align north-eastwards. In some places the ripples are starved, so that underlying gravels show in the troughs. Locally, cross ripples occur on the crests of some ripples. Sand ripples have been identified on several other smooth glaciated pavements and are not restricted to the sand facies, for they have been identified in muddy sands, some in water depths of over 100 m (Eden et al., 1971; 1973). Sand ripples and megaripples have been observed in areas of gravelly and sandy sediments both in the Passage of Oronsay and at the northern end of the Sound of Islay (Farrow et al., 1979).

Pendlebury and Dobson (1976) identified many bedforms in the southern Malin Sea, including sand ribbons and sand waves. The sand-wave fields off the northern Irish coast con-

tain both asymmetrical and symmetrical sand waves; the largest on Hempton's Turbot Bank are up to 30 m high with wavelengths of up to 460 m. The orientations of the sand waves suggest an overall eastward movement, except just west of Benbane Head. Farther north on the Middle Bank, sand ribbons predominate, sand ripples are common, and sporadic sand waves up to 12 m high indicate south-easterly movement.

The hydrodynamic regime in the North Channel is reflected in the form and orientation of sea-bed features. The localities with the highest peak-tidal currents, more than 1.5 m/s, are commonly sediment-free, bare-rock platform or may have transverse gravel ridges about 1 m wide, up to 0.6 m high, and reaching 1.25 km in length (Figure 61). The mobility of these gravel waves is indicated by a lack of epifauna, in contrast to adjacent boulder ridges (Dobson and Haynes, 1973). Over much of the area, asymmetrical sand waves, parabolic sand dunes, and scours about rock outcrops and wrecks, indicate a north-westerly flow, but bedforms on the southern and western flanks of the North Channel suggest movement to the south-east. Pendlebury and Dobson (1976) reported that at the northern entrance to the North Channel, sand ribbons increase in abundance eastwards, whereas sand streams and sand waves are confined to the sea floor between Rathlin Island and the Irish coast. The sand waves exhibit interference patterns close to rock walls at the southern boundary of the report area (Eden et al., 1973).

GAS SEEPAGES

Subsurface shallow gas reported from several parts of the report area is normally associated with deposits of late glacial to Holocene age (Hovland and Judd, 1988; BGS Tiree Quaternary Geology sheet). The gas is believed to be derived predominantly from the decay of organic matter within the sediment, but some may be of petrogenic origin. Methane-gas seepages commonly leave carbonate precipitates at the sea floor, and are associated with local increases in biological activity (Hovland and Judd, 1988). Brown and Farrow (1978) and Farrow (1978) have described protodolomitic concretions around crustacean burrows in Loch Sunart, in the Firth of Clyde and on the shore at Hunterston. Farrow (1978) reported a sample of shelly, fine-grained sands and muds bound by a cement of Recent age recovered from a depth of 120 m southeast of Tiree. Farrow et al. (1979) also described a cemented sand which includes a small, rounded pebble of cemented shell material from a depth of 60 m in the Sound of Jura.

SEA-BED POLLUTION

Parts of the report area lie close to industrial conurbations where the sea bed has in the past suffered the effects of uncontrolled dumping of waste products. The main area of waste dumping at present is the Firth of Clyde; in the sandy muds of the sewage-sludge dumping area in the Sound of Bute, more than tenfold increases are found in the concentrations of certain metals (Burton and Young, 1979). Nuclear radioisotopes are discharged into the sea (Mauchline, 1979) both at the Hunterston power station and at local submarine bases; they also enter the area from the Irish Sea, primarily from Sellafield. At Hunterston, quantities discharged are so low that they cannot be distinguished from the Sellafield effluent and fallout from weapons testing (Mauchline, 1979).

12 Economic geology

There has been little exploitation of offshore resources within the report area, although on the surrounding land there have been many mining operations (see Figure 62 for selected locations), some of which have worked veins or beds extending out under the sea. The majority of ores were exploited in the 18th and 19th centuries, or during the world wars of the 20th century. They have largely become exhausted or uneconomic, but tailings from these workings may have become concentrated in the adjacent coastal waters. Future development of marine extraction techniques may permit exploitation of these secondary deposits.

The coastal and offshore areas are used for a variety of economically related purposes, not least of which are related to the tourist industry. Fish farms abound, and the deep and muddy zones close inshore provide suitable sites for equipment testing, including the Ministry of Defence test ranges in the Inner Sound and the Sound of Raasay. The presence of sheltered deep-water basins led in the 1970s to the development of offshore construction yards at Stornoway, Kishorn and Portavadie, and coastal superquarries can take advantage of transportation by sea, as at Glensanda in Loch Linnhe (Beveridge et al., 1991).

The Garroch Head sewage-sludge disposal site in the Firth of Clyde is an accumulative dump site receiving about 1.7×10^6 tonnes of sludge per year in about 90 m of water; this dumping has resulted in an area of anomalous geochemistry, and has created a high biomass centre that provides a boost for the local fishing industry, although it has severely reduced faunal species diversification (Halcrow et al., 1973).

METALLIC MINERALS

Iron ore has been mined on Raasay (Draper and Draper, 1990) from a band about 2.5 m thick in which chamosite with minor haematite and some siderite occur within the Upper Liassic Shales (Lee, 1920). The deposits may continue offshore, and tailings may be exploitable, for there was severe pollution during the mining activity, when the sea between Raasay and Skye was discoloured (Draper and Draper, 1990). Bands of magnetite are found in the Lewisian of Iona and Tiree (Johnstone and Mykura, 1989), and studies of sea-bed sediments in the Sea of the Hebrides have revealed magnetite concentrations of up to 2 per cent. Samples collected by divers in Loch Scridain, Mull, generally showed less than 1 per cent magnetite, although samples with 3.6 per cent and 5.6 per cent were collected. The 0.6 m-thick Blackstone Ironstone seam in the Ballycastle Coalfield passes laterally eastwards into coal, but there are large reserves below sea level to the west of the workings at Carrickmore (Wilson, 1972).

Galena has been worked at Strontian (Phemister, 1960) for some time, and since 1983 barytes and sphalerite have additionally been exploited (Mason and Mason, 1984). Galena also occurs at Moidart (Johnstone and Mykura, 1989) and on Coll (Wilson and Flett, 1921). Until 1862, veins of galena with some sphalerite were worked on Islay from the Islay Limestone and Esknish Slates, and their commercial prospectivity has recently been re-investigated (Beveridge et al.,

1991). Galena, together with some sphalerite, was found in the copper workings around Loch Fyne, and there are old lead mines at Glen Creran (Wilson and Flett, 1921). Traces of silver and gold have been found in several Scottish lead-zinc veins; a complex lead-zinc-copper ore worked at Stronchullin, near Ardrishaig, showed the exceptional assay value of 4 oz of gold per ton (Macgregor, 1948).

Chalcopyrite, bornite, malachite and brochantite were worked at the head of Loch Kishorn (Phemister, 1960). Copper ores have been mined on Islay and around Loch Fyne (Macgregor, 1948), both as vein and replacement deposits, particularly within calcareous beds of the Dalradian (Duff, 1983). Coastal auriferous copper deposits with minor amounts of silver have been reported at Kilmelford (Harris et al., 1988) and at Gairloch (Jones et al., 1987).

The Interbasaltic Beds of County Antrim have been worked for bauxite (Eyles, 1952), and bauxitic clay also occurs in the Carboniferous rocks of Ayrshire (Cameron and Stephenson, 1985) and Machrihanish (Macgregor, 1948).

A recent study of marine sands off Rum and south-west Skye has revealed significant quantities of olivine and chromite derived from the Tertiary igneous complexes of Rum and the Cuillin of Skye (Gallagher et al., 1989). Within the topmost metre of sand in the submerged deltaic areas south of Rum, the study indicated the presence of 70 000 tonnes of chrome spinel averaging 32 per cent Cr_2O_3 at a grade of nearly 1 per cent (Figure 63). Also present are 1.5 to 2×10^6 tonnes of forsterite-rich olivine (47 per cent MgO) at 25 per cent grade. Other potential byproducts identified are ilmenite and vanadiferous magnetite; traces of platinum group elements have also been detected (Beveridge et al., 1991). Lower concentrations of these minerals were found off south-western Skye, and other basic or ultrabasic bodies may also be sources of placer chromite and olivine deposits, such as at Trotternish (Banner, 1979).

Manganese nodules up to 3 cm in diameter were first discovered on the floor of Loch Fyne in 1878 (Buchanan, 1891), and have since been reported in many sea lochs around the Firth of Clyde (Calvert and Price, 1970). They contain between 30 and 50 per cent MnO_2 and up to 20 per cent Fe_2O_3 as well as significant amounts of other metals, including up to 0.2 per cent zinc, 0.1 per cent lead, 150 ppm of cobalt and 250 ppm nickel, but low concentrations of copper (Deegan et al., 1973). The manganese nodules are probably too sparse to be economic; Allen (1960) measured accumulation rates of manganese of 1 mm in 25 to 60 years on mollusc shells. A neutron-activated gamma detector has been towed along the floor of Loch Fyne to delineate the distribution of the nodules (Thomas et al., 1984).

NONMETALLIC MINERALS

Late Triassic rock salt (halite) has been worked to the south of the report area at or near Carrickfergus for more than a century. Very large reserves of halite are available in the coastal area from Carrickfergus to Larne, and probably extend offshore (Wilson, 1972), although perhaps just outside the

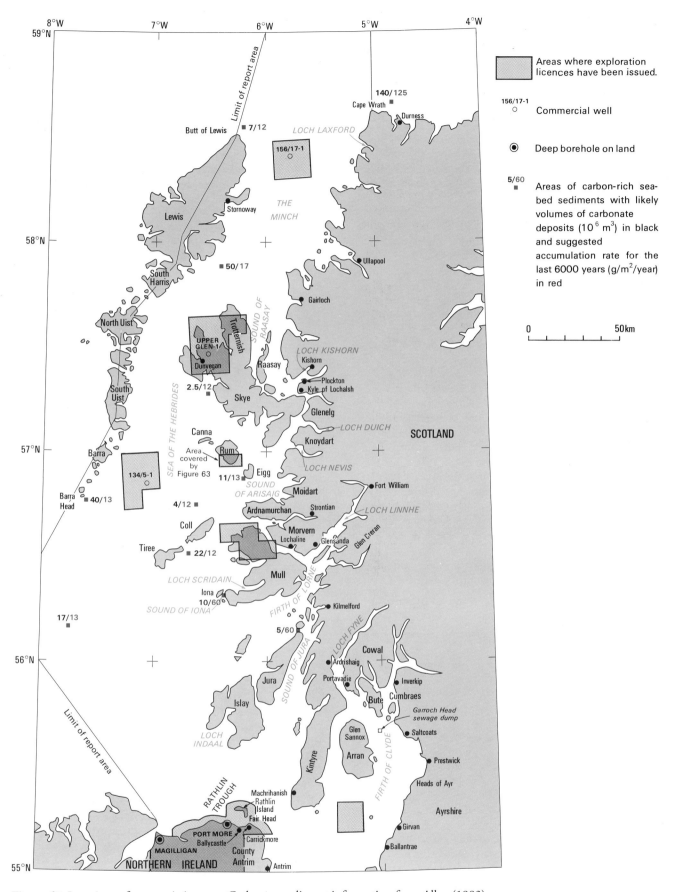

Figure 62 Locations of economic interest. Carbonate sediment information from Allen (1983).

report area. Gypsum and anhydrite may occur within the Permo-Triassic at the southern end of the report area; a 5 m-thick bed of anhydrite has been proved under Belfast (Wilson, 1972), and bands of gypsum up to 4 cm thick, and nodules of anhydrite or gypsum up to 10 cm in size, have been sampled within Triassic sediments at Loch Indaal, off Islay.

The Lower Cambrian Fucoid Beds of the Durness Group crop out along the Moine Thrust, which cuts the coast near Kishorn, and on Skye. They are dolomitic, abnormally rich in potash at an average of 8.5 per cent (Bowie et al., 1966), and locally contain a small percentage of phosphates. The material is being worked for use as a fertiliser (Beveridge et al., 1991).

Barytes has been mined at several localities on land, mainly as gangue within lead-bearing veins, although large amounts have been mined at Strontian for use by the North Sea drilling industry. On Arran, washings from the old Glen Sannox Mines can be seen on the beach in Sannox Bay. Diatomite is formed from freshwater deposits rich in diatoms, being used in the chemical industry and for insulating and refractory bricks; Holocene deposits have been worked in northern Skye, and they also occur on Mull and Eigg (Haldane et al., 1940). In Northern Ireland there are extensive diatomite workings in the Bann Valley of County Antrim. Diatomite may occur where former freshwater sites have become inundated by the sea.

Feldspars have been won from potash-pegmatites in South Harris, and have been found at Durness and near Loch Laxford in Sutherland (Johnstone and Mykura, 1989). Talc of high purity was mined from the Lewisian gneiss on the coast near Glenelg (Phemister, 1960), and from the Dalradian in Cowal (Macgregor, 1948). Mica has been worked at Loch Nevis (Johnstone and Mykura, 1989). The 6 m-thick Upper Cretaceous sandstone on the coast at Lochaline in Morvern is very pure at up to 99.85 per cent silica (Smith, 1989), and is presently the only source in Britain of colourless glass sand suitable for high-grade domestic and decorative glassware.

Shell sands rich in carbonate occur in many parts of the Minches, and are considered as potential sources of lime for the cement industry and for fertiliser. Some beaches comprising nearly pure carbonate have been worked for local use as fertiliser (Ritchie, 1975), and a study of offshore carbonate resources (Allen, 1983) identified several accumulations with greater than 75 per cent $CaCO_3$ within the report area (Figure 62). The most significant deposits are off Cape Wrath, where more than 100×10^6 tonnes were identified at a locality where there is also a very high accumulation rate.

Maërl, a crushed coralline alga, is used as a fertiliser, particularly in France where it is extracted off Brittany (Booth, 1975). The alga, which favours a rocky substrate and clean water, is often erroneously referred to as calcified seaweed. Complete colonies of this purple-coloured living *Lithothamnion*, up to 4 cm in size, are found in the Firth of Clyde. There is a variety of growth forms depending upon environment; delicate, branched, stellate colonies occur in sheltered areas, whereas short, stout, subparallel, branched forms appear in more exposed locations (Deegan et al., 1973). Deegan et al. (1973) report that it is almost universally present south of Kintyre and Arran, and accumulations have been identified off Skye, Kyle of Lochalsh, Plockton, Castlebay (Barra), in the Sound of Iona, the Sound of Jura and around Bute. It occurs as beach corals near Dunvegan on the Isle of Skye and south of the Heads of Ayr, and is found as a raised coral beach on the west side of the Cumbraes.

Reserves of marine sand and gravel occur mainly in the littoral zone, and there has been local extraction from several beaches (Crofts and Ritchie, 1973; Ritchie, 1975; Mather, 1979). Both sand and gravel occur offshore, but few deposits have been exploited, partly because of the abundance of carbonate within many deposits, but also due to the lack of local demand and the existence of extensive, easily accessible aggregate on land. In the upper Firth of Clyde, sand and gravel has been worked off Inverkip; the deposits contain more sand than gravel, but extraction is feasible because of the proximity of markets (Deegan et al., 1973).

FUEL AND ENERGY

The Permo-Triassic and Mesozoic half-graben basins of the report area have been considered as potential sites for hydrocarbon accumulation. The Carboniferous is considered the most likely source rock, for the Jurassic in the Sea of the Hebrides and on Skye may be insufficiently mature to have generated hydrocarbons (Kilenyi and Standley, 1985). Landward exploration licences have been awarded in the Firth of Clyde, the Sea of the Hebrides, The Minch, near the coast of Northern Ireland, and on and around northern Skye (Figure 62). Seismic lines have been shot over much of the area, and although some wells have been sunk, no commercial finds have been reported. BP sank the first offshore well in the report area when they drilled well 156/17-1 in The Minch in 1989. They have subsequently relinquished the licence. On land, the Magilligan borehole (Figure 31) was drilled by the Geological Survey of Northern Ireland in 1963–64, and in 1989 Pentex drilled an exploration well near Dunvegan on Skye (Upper Glen-1). During 1991, Chevron drilled well 134/5-1 in the Sea of the Hebrides (Figure 62).

Carboniferous coal-bearing sediments occur onshore around the Firth of Clyde and Northern Ireland, and in several offshore basins including the Firth of Clyde and the Rathlin Trough. There has been little exploitation of the submarine deposits by coastal collieries. Near Saltcoats, early workings extended under the Firth of Clyde to less than a kilometre from the coast. Collieries near Prestwick exploited the Ayr Hard Seam up to two kilometres offshore, and the Machrihanish

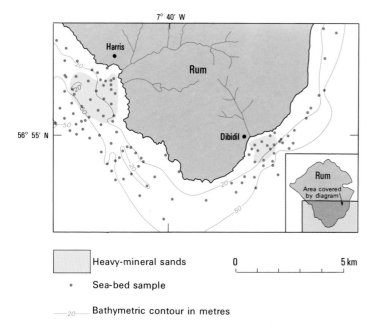

Heavy-mineral sands

• Sea-bed sample

—20— Bathymetric contour in metres

Figure 63 The distribution of sediments off Rum that contain more than 0.12 per cent chromium oxide. See Figure 62 for location of the area covered by the diagram.

Coalfield was worked out to about half a kilometre west of Kintyre. In the Ballycastle Coalfield, worked coals crop out on the coastal cliffs, and fairly large reserves of low-grade Viséan coals occur beneath Fair Head (Wilson, 1972).

Thin, lenticular seams of lignite occur below and within the Tertiary lavas of Mull, Skye, Ardnamurchan, Canna and Northern Ireland, and some have been mined for local use (Woolley and Jermy, 1978). Thick deposits of lignite recently identified in County Antrim within the Tertiary Lough Neagh Clay and along the Tow Valley Fault (Figure 37; Griffith et al., 1987; Parnell and Meighan, 1989) are potentially exploitable commercially; similar deposits may exist off-shore in the contemporaneous Oligocene sedimentary basins of the Sea of the Hebrides.

The exposed coasts and offshore areas of the Inner Hebrides, particularly south of Ardnamurchan, are subjected to significant wave action (Pantin, 1991). They may therefore be suitable locations for wave-energy converters, particularly to supply energy to isolated island communities. One form of wave power undergoing experimental development within the area is an 'artificial blow hole' on Islay (Whittaker, 1991). Tidal power may not become viable as tidal ranges are relatively small within the report area, although there are strong tidal currents in coastal narrows.

References

References to BGS offshore maps are not given here, but an index map showing their distribution in the report area is presented inside the back cover. Most of the references listed below are held in the Library of the British Geological Survey at Keyworth, Nottingham. Copies of the references can be purchased subject to the current copyright legislation.

ABRAHAM, D A, and RITCHIE, J D. 1991. The Darwin Complex, a Tertiary igneous centre in the Northern Rockall Trough. *Scottish Journal of Geology,* Vol. 27, 113–126.

ALLEN, J A. 1960. Manganese deposition on the shells of living molluscs. *Nature, London,* Vol. 185, 336–337.

ALLEN, N H. 1983. Recent temperate carbonate deposits on the continental shelf north and west of Scotland: distribution, sedimentology and reserves. Unpublished PhD thesis, University of Strathclyde.

ANDERSON, F W, and DUNHAM, K C. 1966. The geology of northern Skye. *Memoir of the Geological Survey of Scotland.*

ANDERTON, R. 1979. Slopes, submarine fans, and syn-depositional faults: sedimentology of parts of the middle and upper Dalradian in the SW Highlands of Scotland. 483–488 in The Caledonides of the British Isles reviewed. HARRIS, A L, HOLLAND, C H, and LEAKE, B E (editors). *Special Publication of the Geological Society of London,* No. 8.

— 1985. Sedimentation and tectonics in the Scottish Dalradian. *Scottish Journal of Geology,* Vol. 21, 407–436.

ANDREWS, I J, and six others. 1990. *United Kingdom offshore regional report: the geology of the Moray Firth.* (London: HMSO for the British Geological Survey.)

ARMSTRONG, D. 1957. Dating of some minor intrusions of Ayrshire. *Nature, London,* Vol. 180, 1277.

BALLANTYNE, C K. 1990. The Late Quaternary glacial history of the Trotternish Escarpment, Isle of Skye, Scotland, and its implications for ice-sheet reconstruction. *Proceedings of the Geologists' Association,* Vol. 101, 171–186.

— and SUTHERLAND, D G. 1987. *Wester Ross — field guide.* (Cambridge: Quaternary Research Association.)

— BENN, D I, LOWE, J J, and WALKER, M J C. 1991. *The Quaternary of the Isle of Skye: field guide.* (Cambridge: Quaternary Research Association.)

BAMFORD, D. 1979. Seismic constraints on the deep geology of the Caledonides of northern Britain. 93–96 in The Caledonides of the British Isles reviewed. HARRIS, A L, HOLLAND, C H, and LEAKE, B E (editors). *Special Publication of the Geological Society of London,* No. 8.

— NUNN, K, PRODEHL, C, and JACOB, B. 1978. LISPB–IV. Crustal structure in northern Britain. *Geophysical Journal of the Royal Astronomical Society,* Vol. 54, 43–60.

BANNER, F T. 1979. Seabed resources, potential and actual (excluding hydrocarbons). 547–567 in *The North-West European shelf seas: the sea bed and the sea in motion — II. Physical and chemical oceanography, and physical resources.* BANNER, F T, COLLINS, M B, and MASSIE, K S (editors). (Amsterdam: Elsevier.)

— and CULVER, S J. 1979. Sediments of the North-Western European Shelf. 271–300 in *The North-West European shelf seas: the sea bed and the sea in motion — I. Geology and sedimentology.* BANNER, F T, COLLINS, M B, and MASSIE, K S (editors). (Amsterdam: Elsevier.)

BARBER, P L, DOBSON, M R, and WHITTINGTON, R J. 1979. The geology of the Firth of Lorne, as determined by seismic and dive sampling methods. *Scottish Journal of Geology,* Vol. 15, 217–230.

BELL, B R, and HARRIS, J W. 1986. *An excursion guide to the geology of the Isle of Skye.* (Glasgow: McCorquodale.)

BENN, D I, and DAWSON, A G. 1987. A Devensian glaciomarine sequence in western Islay, Inner Hebrides. *Scottish Journal of Geology,* Vol. 23, 175–187.

BEVERIDGE, R, BROWN, S, GALLAGHER, M J, and MERRITT, J W. 1991. Economic geology. In *The geology of Scotland* (3rd edition). CRAIG, G Y (editor). (Bath: Geological Society Publishing House.)

BINNS, P E, HARLAND, R, and HUGHES, M J. 1974a. Glacial and post-glacial sedimentation in the Sea of the Hebrides. *Nature, London,* Vol. 48, 751–754.

— McQUILLIN, R, and KENOLTY, N. 1974b. The geology of the Sea of the Hebrides. *Report of the Institute of Geological Sciences,* No. 73/14.

BIRNIE, J. 1983. Tolsta Head: further investigations of the interstadial deposit. *Quaternary Newsletter,* Vol. 41, 18–25.

BISHOP, P. 1977. Glacial and post-glacial sedimentation in the Minches, North West Scotland. Unpublished PhD thesis, University of London.

— and JONES, E J W. 1979. Patterns of glacial and post-glacial sedimentation in the Minches, North-West Scotland. 89–194 in *The North-West European shelf seas: the sea bed and the sea in motion — 1. Geology and sedimentology.* BANNER, F T, COLLINS, M B, and MASSIE, K S (editors). (Amsterdam: Elsevier.)

BLACKBOURN, G. 1981. Probable Old Red Sandstone conglomerates around Tongue and adjacent areas, north Sutherland. *Scottish Journal of Geology,* Vol. 17, 103–118.

BLUCK, B J. 1978. Sedimentation in a late orogenic basin: the Old Red Sandstone of the Midland Valley of Scotland. 151–162 in Crustal evolution in north western Britain and adjacent regions. BOWES, D R, and LEAKE, B E (editors). *Geological Journal Special Issue,* No. 1.

— 1984. Pre-Carboniferous history of the Midland Valley of Scotland. *Transactions of the Royal Society of Edinburgh: Earth Sciences,* Vol. 75, 275–295.

BOOTH, E. 1975. Seaweeds in industry. 219–268 in *Chemical oceanography.* Vol. 4. RILEY, J P, and SKIRROW, G (editors). (London: Academic Press.)

BOTT, M H P, ARMOUR, A R, HIMSWORTH, E M, MURPHY, T, and WYLIE, G. 1979. An explosion seismology investigation of the continental margin west of the Hebrides, Scotland, at 58°N. *Tectonophysics,* Vol. 59, 217–231.

— and TUSON, J. 1973. Deep structure beneath the Tertiary volcanic regions of Skye, Mull and Ardnamurchan, north-west Scotland. *Nature Physical Science, London,* Vol. 242, 114–116.

BOULTER, M C, and KVACEK, Z. 1989. The Palaeocene flora of the Isle of Mull. *Palaeontological Association Special Paper,* No. 42.

BOULTON, G S, CHROSTON, N P, and JARVIS, J. 1981. A marine seismic study of late Quaternary sedimentation and inferred glacier fluctuations along western Inverness-shire, Scotland. *Boreas,* Vol. 10, 39–51.

BOWES, D R, and HOPGOOD, A M. 1975. Structure of the gneiss complex of Inishtrahull, Co. Donegal. *Proceedings of the Royal Irish Academy,* Vol. 75, 369–390.

BOWIE, S H, DAWSON, J, GALLAGHER, M J, and OSTLE, D. 1966. Potassium-rich sediments in the Cambrian of northwest Scotland. *Transactions of the Institute for Mining and Metallurgy,* Vol. 75, B125–B145.

BREWER, J A, and five others. 1983. BIRPS deep seismic reflection studies of the British Caledonides. *Nature, London,* Vol. 305, 206–210.

— and SMYTHE, D K. 1984. MOIST and the continuity of crustal reflector geometry along the Caledonian–Appalachian orogen. *Journal of the Geological Society of London,* Vol. 141, 105–120.

— — 1986. Deep structure of the foreland to the Caledonian orogen, NW Scotland: results of the BIRPS WINCH profile. *Tectonics,* Vol. 5, 171–194.

BRITISH GEOLOGICAL SURVEY. 1987. Arran (Special District). Solid. 1:50 000. (Southampton Ordnance Survey for British Geological Survey.)

BROOK, M, BREWER, M S, and POWELL, D. 1977. Grenville events in the Moine rocks of the northern Highlands, Scotland. *Journal of the Geological Society of London,* Vol. 133, 489–496.

BROWN, B J, and FARROW, G E. 1978. Recent dolomitic concretions of Crustacean burrow origin from Loch Sunart, west coast of Scotland. *Journal of Sedimentary Petrology,* Vol. 48, 825–834.

BROWN, P E. 1983. Caledonian and earlier magmatism. 167–204 in *The geology of Scotland* (2nd edition). CRAIG, G Y (editor). (Edinburgh: Scottish Academic Press.)

BROWNE, M A E, and McMILLAN, A A. 1984. Shoreline inheritance and coastal history in the Firth of Clyde. *Scottish Journal of Geology,* Vol. 20, 119–120.

BUCHANAN, J Y. 1891. On the composition of oceanic and littoral manganese nodules. *Transactions of the Royal Society of Edinburgh,* Vol. 36, 459–483.

BURTON, J D, and YOUNG, M L. 1979. Trace metals in the shelf seas of the British Isles. 494–516 in *The North-West European shelf seas: the sea bed and the sea in motion — II. Physical and chemical oceanography, and physical resources.* BANNER, F T, COLLINS, M B, and MASSIE, K S (editors). (Amsterdam: Elsevier.)

CALVERT, S E, and PRICE, N B. 1970. Composition of manganese nodules and manganese carbonates from Loch Fyne, Scotland. *Contributions to Mineralogy and Petrology,* Vol. 29, 215–233.

CAMERON, I B, and STEPHENSON, D. 1985. *British regional geology: the Midland Valley of Scotland* (3rd edition). (London: HMSO for British Geological Survey.)

CAMERON, T D J, STOKER, M S, and LONG, D. 1987. The history of Quaternary sedimentation in the UK sector of the North Sea Basin. *Journal of the Geological Society of London,* Vol. 144, 43–58.

— and six others. 1992. *United Kingdom offshore regional report: the geology of the southern North Sea.* (London: HMSO for British Geological Survey.)

CARTER, R W G, DEVOY, R J N, and SHAW, J. 1989. Late Holocene sea levels in Ireland. *Journal of Quaternary Science,* Vol. 4, 7–24.

CASTON, G F. 1975. Igneous dykes and associated scour hollows of the North Channel, Irish Sea. *Marine Geology,* Vol. 18, M77–M85.

— 1976. The floor of the North Channel, Irish Sea: a side-scan sonar survey. *Report of the Institute of Geological Sciences,* No. 76/7.

CHADWICK, R A, and HOLLIDAY, D W. 1991. Deep crustal structure and Carboniferous basin development within the Iapetus convergence zone, northern England. *Journal of the Geological Society of London,* Vol. 148, 41–54.

CHESHER, J A, DEEGAN, C E, ARDUS, D A, BINNS, P E and FANNIN, N G T. 1972. IGS marine drilling with *m.v. Whitethorn* in Scottish waters 1970–1971. *Report of the Institute of Geological Sciences,* No. 72/10.

— SMYTHE, D K, and BISHOP, P. 1983. The geology of the Minches, Inner Sound and Sound of Raasay. *Report of the Institute of Geological Sciences,* No. 83/6.

CLIMAP, 1976. The surface of the Ice-Age. *Earth Science, New York,* Vol. 191, 1131–1137.

COLE, G A J, and CROOK, T. 1910. On the rock specimens dredged from the floor of the Atlantic off the coast of Ireland. *Memoir of the Geological Survey of Ireland.*

COWARD, M P. 1990. The Precambrian, Caledonian and Variscan framework to NW Europe. 1–34 in Tectonic events responsible for Britain's oil and gas reserves. HARDMAN, R F P, and BROOKS, J (editors). *Special Publication of the Geological Society of London,* No. 55.

— ENFIELD, M A, and FISCHER, M W. 1989. Devonian basins of Northern Scotland: extension and inversion related to late Caledonian–Variscan tectonics. 275–308 in Inversion tectonics. COOPER, M A, and WILLIAMS, S G D (editors). *Special Publication of the Geological Society of London,* No. 44.

CRAIG, R. 1887. On the Post-Pliocene beds of the Irvine valley, Kilmaurs and Dreghorn districts. *Transactions of the Geological Society of Glasgow,* Vol 8, 213–226.

CROFTS, R, and RITCHIE, W. 1973. *Beaches of mainland Argyll.* (Aberdeen: University of Aberdeen.)

CROSSKEY, H W, and ROBERTSON, D. 1871. On the post-Tertiary fossiliferous beds of Scotland. *Transactions of the Geological Society of Glasgow,* Vol. 2, 267–282 and Vol. 3, 113–129 and 321–341.

CURRY, D, and six others. 1978. A correlation of Tertiary rocks in the British Isles. *Special Report of the Geological Society of London,* No. 12.

DALY, J S, MUIR, R J, and CLIFF, R A. 1991. A precise U-Pb zircon age for the Inishtrahull syenitic gneiss, County Donegal, Ireland. *Journal of the Geological Society,* Vol. 148, 639–642.

DAVIES, C M. 1987. Seismic stratigraphical sequences in the Lundy Tertiary basin, Bristol Channel. *Proceedings of the Geologists' Association,* Vol. 98, 355–366.

DAVIES, H C, DOBSON, M R, and WHITTINGTON, R J. 1984. A revised seismic stratigraphy for Quaternary deposits on the inner continental shelf west of Scotland between 55°30'N and 57°30'N. *Boreas,* Vol. 13, 49–66.

DAWSON, A G. 1980. Shore erosion by frost; an example from the Scottish Lateglacial. 45–53 in *Studies in the Lateglacial of North-West Europe.* LOWE J J, GRAY, J M, and ROBINSON, J E (editors). (Oxford: Pergamon Press.)

— (editor). 1988. *Late Quaternary sea levels and crustal deformation, Scotland.* International Union for Quaternary Research, Subcommission on shorelines for NW Europe, Symposium. (Coventry: Coventry Polytechnic.)

DEARNLEY, R. 1962. An outline of the Lewisian complex of the Outer Hebrides in relation to that of the Scottish mainland. *Quarterly Journal of the Geological Society of London,* Vol. 18, 143–176.

DEEGAN, C E. 1978. Boreholes and outcrop sampling in sheet 55°N/6°W. 65–76 in The solid geology of the Clyde Sheet (55°N/6°W). McLEAN, A C, and DEEGAN, C E (editors). *Report of the Institute of Geological Sciences,* No. 78/9.

— KIRBY, R, RAE, I, and FLOYD, R. 1973. The superficial deposits of the Firth of Clyde and its sea lochs. *Report of the Institute of Geological Sciences,* No. 73/9.

DICKIN, A P, and BOWES, D R. 1991. Isotopic evidence for the extent of early Proterozoic basement in Scotland and northwest Ireland. *Geological Magazine,* Vol. 128, 385–388.

DOBINSON, A. 1978. Geophysical studies south and west of Kintyre. 77–91 in The solid geology of the Clyde Sheet (55°N/6°W). McLEAN, A C, and DEEGAN, C E (editors). *Report of the Institute of Geological Sciences,* No. 78/9.

DOBSON, M R, and EVANS, D. 1974. Geological structure of the Malin Sea. *Journal of the Geological Society of London,* Vol. 130, 475–478.

— — and WHITTINGTON, R J. 1975. The offshore extensions of the Loch Gruinart Fault, Islay. *Scottish Journal of Geology,* Vol. 11, 23–35.

— and HAYNES, J R. 1973. Association of foraminifera with hydroids on the deep shelf. *Micropalaeontology,* Vol. 19, 78–90.

— and WHITTINGTON, R J. 1987. The geology of Cardigan Bay. *Proceedings of the Geologists' Association,* Vol. 98, 331–353.

— — 1992. Aspects of the geology of the Malin sea area. *In* Post-Devonian basin development in the north-west seaboard of the British Isles. PARNELL, J (editor). *Special Publication of the Geological Society of London,* No 62.

DRAPER, L, and DRAPER, P. 1990. *The Raasay iron mine.* (Dingwall: Laurence and Pamela Draper.)

DUFF, P Mc L D. 1983. Economic geology. 425–454 in *The geology of Scotland* (2nd edition). CRAIG, G Y (editor). (Edinburgh: Scottish Academic Press.)

DURANT, G P. 1979. Igneous bodies sampled by diving and dredging in the eastern Malin Sea. Appendix 3 *in* The geology of the Malin Sea. EVANS, D, KENOLTY, N, DOBSON, M R, and WHITTINGTON, R J. 1979. *Report of the Institute of Geological Sciences,* No. 79/15.

— DOBSON, M R, KOKELAAR, B P, MCINTYRE, R M, and REA, W J. 1976. Preliminary report on the nature and age of the Blackstones Bank igneous centre, western Scotland. *Journal of the Geological Society of London,* Vol. 132, 319–326.

— KOKELAAR, B P, and WHITTINGTON, R J. 1982. The Blackstones Bank igneous centre, western Scotland. 297–308 in *Proceedings of the 6th Symposium of the Confédération Mondiale des Activities Subaquatique.* (London: Natural Environment Research Council.)

EARLE, M M, JANKOWSKI, E J, and VANN, I R. 1989. Structural and stratigraphic evolution of the Faeroe–Shetland Channel and Northern Rockall Trough. 461–489 in Extensional tectonics and stratigraphy of the North Atlantic margins. TANKARD A J, AND BALKWILL, H R (editors) *Memoir of the American Association of Petroleum Geologists,* No. 46.

EDEN, R A, ARDUS, D A, BINNS, P E, McQUILLIN, R, and WILSON, J B. 1971. Geological investigations with a manned submersible off the west coast of Scotland 1969–1970. *Report of the Institute of Geological Sciences,* No. 71/16.

— DEEGAN, C E, RHYS, G H, WRIGHT, J E, and DOBSON, M R. 1973. Geological investigations with a manned submersible in the Irish Sea and off western Scotland 1971. *Report of the Institute of Geological Sciences,* No. 73/2.

EDWARDS, P G. 1982. Ecology and distribution of selected foraminiferal species in the North Minch Channel, northwestern Scotland. 111–139 in *Aspects of micropalaeontology; papers presented to Professor Tom Barnard.* BANNER, F T (editor). (London: George Allen and Unwin.)

EMELEUS, C H, 1983. Tertiary igneous activity. 357–397 in *The geology of Scotland* (2nd edition). CRAIG, G Y (editor). (Edinburgh: Scottish Academic Press.)

— 1985. The Tertiary lavas and sediments of northwest Rhum, Inner Hebrides. *Geological Magazine,* Vol. 122, 419–437.

EVANS, D. 1974. Geophysical studies in the Malin Sea. Unpublished PhD thesis, University of Wales.

— ABRAHAM, D A, and HITCHEN, K. 1989. The Geikie igneous centre, west of Lewis: its structure and influence on Tertiary geology. *Scottish Journal of Geology,* Vol. 25, 339–352.

— CHESHER, J A, DEEGAN, C E, and FANNIN, N G T. 1981. The offshore geology of Scotland in relation to the IGS shallow drilling programme, 1970–1978. *Report of the Institute of Geological Sciences,* No. 81/12.

— HALLSWORTH, C, JOLLEY, D W, and MORTON, A C. 1991. Late Oligocene terrestrial sediments from a small basin in the Little Minch. *Scottish Journal of Geology,* Vol. 27, 33–40.

— KENOLTY, N, DOBSON, M R, and WHITTINGTON, R J. 1979a. The geology of the Malin Sea. *Report of the Institute of Geological Sciences,* No. 79/15.

— and RUCKLEY, N A. 1980. The geology and origin of narrow closed channels in the Sound of Jura. *Scottish Journal of Geology,* Vol. 16, 65–72.

— and WHITTINGTON, R J. 1976. The submarine extensions of the Thorr and Fanad plutons, County Donegal. *Proceedings of the Royal Irish Acadamy,* Vol. 76B, 111–120.

— WILKINSON, G C, and CRAIG, D L. 1979b. The Tertiary sediments of the Canna Basin, Sea of the Hebrides. *Scottish Journal of Geology,* Vol. 15, 329–332.

EYLES, V I. 1952. The composition and origin of the Antrim laterites and bauxites. *Memoir of the Geological Survey of Northern Ireland (Mineral Resources).*

FAIRBANKS, R G. 1989. A 17 000-year glacio-eustatic sea level record: influence of glacial melting rates on the Younger Dryas event and deep-ocean circulation. *Nature, London,* Vol. 342, 637–642.

FANNIN, N G T. 1989. BGS offshore investigations 1966–87. *British Geological Survey Technical Report,* WB/89/2.

FARROW, G E. 1978. Recent sediments and sedimentation in the Inner Hebrides. *Proceedings of the Royal Society of Edinburgh,* Vol. 83B, 91–105.

— CUCCI, M, and SCOFFIN, T P. 1978. Calcareous sediments on the nearshore continental shelf of western Scotland. *Proceedings of the Royal Society of Edinburgh,* Vol. 76B, 55–76.

— and FYFE, J A. 1988. Bioerosion and carbonate mud production on high-latitude shelves. 281–297 *in* Non-tropical shelf carbonates — modern and ancient. NELSON, C S (editor). *Sedimentary Geology,* Vol. 60.

— SCOFFIN, T, BROWN, B, and CUCCI, M. 1979. An underwater television survey of facies variations on the inner Scottish shelf between Colonsay, Islay and Jura. *Scottish Journal of Geology,* Vol. 15, 13–29.

FARUQUEE, A R. 1972. A geophysical study of the submerged Blackstones Igneous Centre and Great Glen Fault, SW of Mull. Unpublished PhD thesis, University of Glasgow.

FETTES, D J. 1979. A metamorphic map of the British and Irish Caledonides. 307–321 *in* The Caledonides of the British Isles reviewed. HARRIS, A L, HOLLAND, C H, and LEAKE, B E (editors). *Special Publication of the Geological Society of London,* No. 8.

— and HARRIS, A L. 1986. The Caledonian geology of the Scottish Highlands. 303–334 in *Synthesis of the Caledonian rocks of Britain.* FETTES, D J, and HARRIS, A L (editors). (Dordrecht: Reidel Publishing Company.)

— and MENDUM, J R. 1987. The evolution of the Lewisian complex in the Outer Hebrides. 27–44 *in* Evolution of the Lewisian and comparable Precambrian high grade terrains. PARK, R G, and TARNEY, J (editors). *Special Publication of the Geological Society of London ,* No. 27.

— — SMITH, D I, and WATSON, J V. 1992. Geology of the Outer Hebrides. *Memoir of the British Geological Survey.*

FITCHES, W R, and MALTMAN, A J. 1984. Tectonic development and stratigraphy at the western margin of the Caledonides: Islay and Colonsay, Scotland. *Transactions of the Royal Society of Edinburgh: Earth Sciences,* Vol. 75, 365–382.

— MUIR, R J, MALTMAN, A J, and BENTLEY, M R. 1990. Is the Colonsay — west Islay block of SW Scotland an allochthonous terrace? Evidence from Dalradian tillite clasts. *Journal of the Geological Society of London,* Vol. 147, 417–420.

FLETCHER, B N. 1975. A new Tertiary basin east of Lundy Island. *Journal of the Geological Society of London,* Vol. 131, 223–226.

FLETCHER, T P. 1977. Lithostratigraphy of the Chalk (Ulster White Limestone Formation) in Northern Ireland. *Report of the Institute of Geological Sciences,* No. 77/24.

FOLK, R L. 1954. The distinction between grain size and mineral composition in sedimentary-rock nomenclature. *Journal of Geology,* Vol. 62. 344–359.

FRANCIS, E H. 1978. The Midland Valley rift, seen in connection with the late Palaeozoic European Rift System. 133–148 *in* Tectonics and geophysics of continental rifts. RAMBERG, I B, and NEUMANN, E R (editors). *NATO Advanced Study Institute, Series C, Mathematical and Physical Sciences Series,* No. 37.

FYFE, J A, ABBOTS, I, and CROSBY, A. 1981. The subcrop of the mid-Mesozoic unconformity in the UK area. 236–244 in *Petroleum geology of the continental shelf of North-West Europe.* ILLING, L V, and HOBSON, G D (editors). (London: Heyden and Son.)

GALLAGHER, M J, and eleven others. 1989. Marine deposits of chromite and olivine, Inner Hebrides of Scotland. *British Geological Survey Technical Report*, WB/89/13.

GATLIFF, R W, HITCHEN, K, RITCHIE, J D, and SMYTHE, D K. 1984. Internal structure of the Erlend Tertiary volcanic complex, north of Shetland, revealed by seismic reflection. *Journal of the Geological Society*, Vol. 141, 555–562.

GEIKIE, J. 1878. On the glacial phenomena of the Long Island, or Outer Hebrides. Second Paper. *Quarterly Journal of the Geological Society of London*, Vol. 34, 819–870.

GEOLOGICAL SURVEY OF NORTHERN IRELAND. 1984. *Mineral Exploration Programme.* Vol. 1–9. (Belfast: GSNI.)

GEORGE, T N. 1967. Landform and structure in Ulster. *Scottish Journal of Geology*, Vol. 3, 413–48.

GERARD, J P, and BOILLOT, G. 1977. Geology of the north Irish continental shelf. *Marine Geology*, Vol. 23, 171–179.

GIBB, F G F, and HENDERSON, C M B. 1984. The structure of the Shiant Isles sill complex, Outer Hebrides. *Scottish Journal of Geology*, Vol. 20, 21–30.

GRAHAM, D K, HARLAND, R, GREGORY, D M, LONG, D, and MORTON, A C. 1990. The biostratigraphy and chronostratigraphy of BGS borehole 78/4, North Minch, Scotland. *Scottish Journal of Geology*, Vol. 26, 65–76.

GRAY, J M, and SUTHERLAND, D G. 1977. The 'Oban–Ford Moraine': a reappraisal. 33–44 in *Studies in the Scottish Lateglacial environment.* GRAY, J M, and LOWE, J J (editors). (Oxford: Pergamon Press.)

GRAY, W D T, and BARNES, G. 1981. The Heather oil field. 335–341 in *Petroleum geology of the continental shelf of North-West Europe.* ILLING, L V, and HOBSON, G D (editors). (London: Heyden and Son.)

GREIG, D C. 1971. *British regional geology: the south of Scotland* (3rd edition). (Edinburgh: HMSO for Institute of Geological Sciences.)

GRIFFITH, A E, LEGG, I C, and MITCHELL, W I. 1987. Mineral resources. 43–58 in *Province, city and people; Belfast and its region.* BUCHANAN, R H, and WALKER, B M (editors). (Belfast: Greystone Books in association with the Northern Ireland Committee of the British Association for the Advancement of Science.)

GUNN, W. 1903. The geology of north Arran, south Bute and the Cumbraes. *Memoir of the Geological Survey of Great Britain,* Sheet 21.

HALCROW, W, MACKAY, D W, and THORNTON, I. 1973. The distribution of trace metals and fauna in the Firth of Clyde in relation to the disposal of sewage sludge. *Journal of the Marine Biological Association, UK.* Vol. 53, 721–739.

HALDANE, D, EYLES, V A, and DAVIDSON, C F. 1940. Diatomite. *Wartime Pamphlet of the Geological Survey of Great Britain,* No. 5.

HALL, A M. 1991. Pre-Quaternary landscape evolution in the Scottish Highlands. *Transactions of the Royal Society of Edinburgh: Earth Sciences,* Vol. 82, 1–26.

HALL, J, BREWER, J A, MATTHEWS, D H, and WARNER, M R. 1984. Crustal structure across the Caledonides from the 'WINCH' seismic reflection profile: influences on the evolution of the Midland Valley of Scotland. *Transactions of the Royal Society of Edinburgh,* Vol. 75, 97–109.

— and RASHID, B M. 1977. A possible submerged wave-cut platform in the Firth of Lorne. *Scottish Journal of Geology,* Vol. 13, 285–288.

HALLAM, A. 1978. Eustatic cycles in the Jurassic. *Palaeogeography, Palaeoclimatology and Palaeoecology,* Vol. 23, 1–32.

— 1981. A revised sea-level curve for the early Jurassic. *Journal of the Geological Society of London,* Vol. 138, 753–743.

— 1983. Jurassic, Cretaceous and Tertiary sediments. 343–356 in *The geology of Scotland* (2nd edition). CRAIG, G Y (editor). (Edinburgh: Scottish Academic Press.)

— 1984. Pre-Quaternary sea-level changes. *Annual Review of Earth Sciences,* Vol. 12, 205–243.

HAQ, B U, HARDENBOL, J, and VAIL, P R. 1987. The chronology of fluctuating sea level since the Triassic. *Science, New York,* Vol. 235, 1136–1167.

HARKNESS, D D, and WILSON, H W. 1974. Scottish Universities Research and Reactor Centre radiocarbon measurements 11. *Radiocarbon,* Vol. 16, 238–251.

HARRIS, A L, and four others. 1978. Ensialic basin sedimentation: the Dalradian Supergroup. 115–138 *in* Crustal evolution in northwestern Britain and adjacent regions. BOWES, D R, and LEAKE B E (editors). *Geological Journal Special Issue*, No. 10.

— and PITCHER, W S. 1975. The Dalradian Supergroup. 52–77 *in* A correlation of the Precambrian rocks of the British Isles. HARRIS, A L, and five others (editors). *Special Report of the Geological Society of London,* No. 6.

HARRIS, M, KAY, E A, WIDNALL, M A, JONES, E M, and STEELE, G B. 1988. Geology and mineralisation of the Lagalochan intrusive complex, western Argyll, Scotland. *Transactions of the Institution of Mining and Metallurgy,* Vol. 97, B15–B21.

HASZELDINE, R S, and RUSSELL, M J. 1987. The Late Carboniferous northern North Atlantic Ocean: implications for hydrocarbon exploration from Britain to the Arctic. 1163–1175 in *Petroleum geology of North West Europe.* BROOKS, J, and GLENNIE, K W (editors). (London: Graham and Trotman.)

HENDERSON, W G, and ROBERTSON, A H F. 1982. The Highland Border rocks and their relation to marginal basin development in the Scottish Caledonides. *Journal of the Geological Society of London,* Vol. 139, 435–452.

HIGGINS, A K, and PHILLIPS, W E A. 1979. East Greenland Caledonides — an extension of the British Caledonides. 19–32 *in* The Caledonides of the British Isles reviewed. HARRIS, A L, HOLLAND, C H, and LEAKE, B E (editors). *Special Publication of the Geological Society of London,* No. 8.

HOLLAND, C H. 1981. Devonian. 121–146 in *A geology of Ireland.* HOLLAND, C H (editor). (Edinburgh: Scottish Academic Press.)

HOVLAND, M, and JUDD, A G. 1988. *Seabed pockmarks and seepages: impact on geology, biology and the marine environment.* (London: Graham and Trotman.)

HUDSON, J D. 1963. The recognition of salinity-controlled mollusc assemblages in the Great Esturine Series of the Inner Hebrides. *Palaeontology,* Vol. 6, 318–326.

HUTTON, D H W. 1979. Dalradian structure in the Creeslough area, NW Donegal, Ireland. 239–241 *in* The Caledonides of the British Isles reviewed. HARRIS, A L, HOLLAND, C H, and LEAKE, B E (editors). *Special Publication of the Geological Society of London,* No. 8.

— 1987. Strike-slip terranes and a model for the evolution of the British and Irish Caledonides. *Geological Magazine,* Vol. 124, 405–425.

JARDINE, W G. 1977. The Quaternary marine record in south west Scotland and the Scottish Hebrides. 99–118 in *The Quaternary history of the Irish Sea.* KIDSON, C, and TOOLEY, M J (editors). (Liverpool: Seel House Press.)

— and five others. 1988. A late Middle Devensian interstadial site at Sourlie, near Irvine, Strathclyde. *Scottish Journal of Geology,* Vol. 24, 288–295.

JEHU, T J, and CRAIG, R M. 1934. Geology of the Outer Hebrides. Part 4. North Harris and Lewis. *Transactions of the Royal Society of Edinburgh,* Vol. 57, 839–874.

JOHNSON, M R W. 1983. Torridonian–Moine. 49–75 in *The geology of Scotland* (2nd edition). CRAIG, G Y (editor). (Edinburgh: Scottish Academic Press.)

— and FROST, R T C. 1977. Fault and lineament patterns in the south Highlands of Scotland. *Geologie en Mijnbouw,* Vol. 56, 287–294.

— SANDERSON, D J, and SOPER, N J. 1979. Deformation of the Caledonides of England, Ireland and Scotland. 165–186 *in* The Caledonides of the British Isles reviewed. HARRIS, A L, HOLLAND, C

H, and LEAKE, B E (editors). *Special Publication of the Geological Society of London,* No. 8.

JOHNSTONE, G S. 1966. *British regional geology: the Grampian Highlands* (3rd edition). (Edinburgh: HMSO for the Geological Survey and Museum.)

— and MYKURA, W. 1989. *British regional geology: the Northern Highlands of Scotland* (4th edition). (London: HMSO for British Geological Survey.)

— SMITH, D I, and HARRIS, A L. 1969. The Moinian assemblage of Scotland. 159–180 in North Atlantic — geology and continental drift: a symposium. KAY, M (editor). *Memoir of the American Association of Petroleum Geologists,* Vol. 12.

JONES, E J W, PERRY, R G, and WILD, J L. 1986 Geology of the Hebridean margin of the Rockall Trough. *Proceedings of the Royal Society of Edinburgh,* Vol. 88B, 27–51.

JONES, E M, RICE, C M, and TWEEDIE, J R. 1987. Lower Proterozoic stratiform sulphide deposits in the Loch Maree Group, Gairloch, northwest Scotland. *Transactions of the Institution of Mining and Metallurgy,* Vol. 96, B128–B140.

KENNEDY, M J. 1979. The continuation of the Canadian Appalachians into the Caledonides of Britain and Ireland. 33–64 *in* The Caledonides of the British Isles reviewed. HARRIS, A L, HOLLAND, C H, and LEAKE, B E (editors). *Special Publication of the Geological Society of London,* No. 8.

KILENYI, T, and STANDLEY, B. 1985. Petroleum prospects in the northwest seaboard of Scotland. *Oil and Gas Journal,* Oct 7 1985, 100–108.

KIRTON, S R, and HITCHEN, K. 1987. Timing and style of crustal extension north of the Scottish mainland. 501–510 *in* Continental extensional tectonics. COWARD, M P, DEWEY, J F, and HANCOCK, P L (editors). *Special Publication of the Geological Society of London,* No. 28.

KLEMPERER, S L, RYAN, P D, and SNYDER, D B. 1991. A deep seismic reflection transect across the Irish Caledonides. *Journal of the Geological Society of London,* Vol. 148, 149–164.

KNOX, R W O'B. 1977. Upper Jurassic pyroclastic rocks in Skye, West Scotland. *Nature, London,* Vol. 265. 323–324.

__ and MORTON, A C. 1983. Stratigraphical distribution of early Palaeogene pyroclastic deposits in the North Sea Basin. *Proceedings of the Yorkshire Geological Society,* Vol. 44, 145–151.

— — 1988. The record of early Tertiary North Atlantic volcanism in sediments of the North Sea Basin. 407–419 *in* Early Tertiary volcanism and the opening of the NE Atlantic. MORTON, A C, and PARSON, L M (editors). *Special Publication of the Geological Society of London,* No. 39.

KÜRSTEN, M. 1957. The metamorphic and tectonic history of parts of the Outer Hebrides. *Transactions of the Edinburgh Geological Society,* Vol. 17, 1–31.

LAILEY, M, STEIN, A L, and RESTON, T J. 1989. The Outer Hebrides Fault: a major Proterozoic structure in NW Britain. *Journal of the Geological Society of London,* Vol. 146, 253–259.

LE COEUR, C. 1988. Late Tertiary warping and erosion in western Scotland. *Geografiska Annaler,* Vol. 70A, 361–368.

LEE, G W. 1920. The Mesozoic rocks of Applecross, Raasay and north-east Skye. *Memoir of the Geological Survey of Scotland.*

LEGGETT, J K, McKERROW, W S, and SOPER, N J. 1983. A model for the crustal evolution of southern Scotland. *Tectonics,* Vol. 2, 187–210.

LOVELL, J P B. 1983. Permian and Triassic. 325–342 in *The geology of Scotland* (2nd edition). CRAIG, G Y (editor). (Edinburgh: Scottish Academic Press.)

LOWE, J J. 1984. A critical evaluation of the pollen-stratigraphic investigations of pre-late Devensian sites in Scotland. *Quaternary Science Reviews,* Vol. 3, 405–432.

MACGREGOR, A G. 1948. *British regional geology: the Grampian Highlands* (2nd edition). (Edinburgh: HMSO for Geological Survey of Great Britain.)

MACGREGOR, M. 1965. *Excursion guide of the geology of Arran.* (Glasgow: Glasgow University Press.)

MACINTYRE, R M, VAN BREEMAN, O, BOWES, D R, and HOPGOOD, A M. 1975. Isotopic study of the gneiss complex, Inishtrahull, Co. Donegal. *Scientific Proceedings of the Royal Dublin Society,* Vol. 5, Series A, 301–309.

MACKINNON, A. 1974. The Madadh Rocks: a Tertiary olivine dolerite sill in the Outer Hebrides. *Scottish Journal of Geology,* Vol. 10, 67–70.

MANNING, P I, and WILSON, H E. 1975. The stratigraphy of the Larne borehole, County Antrim. *Bulletin of the Geological Survey of Great Britain,* Vol. 50, 1–50.

MARCANTONIO, F, DICKIN, A P, McNUTT, R H, and HEAMAN, L M. 1988. A 1800-million-year old Proterozoic gneiss terrane in Islay with implications for the crustal structure and evolution of Britain. *Nature, London,* Vol. 355, 62–64.

MASON, P W, and MASON, J E. 1984. The Strontian barytes project — a case study. *Transactions of the Institution of Mining and Metallurgy,* Vol. A133–A135.

MATHER, A S. 1979. *Beaches of southwest Scotland.* (Aberdeen: University of Aberdeen.)

MAUCHLINE, J. 1979. Artificial radioisotopes in the marginal seas of northwestern Europe. 517–542 in *The North-West European shelf seas: the sea bed and the sea in motion — II. Physical and chemical oceanography, and physical resources.* BANNER, F T, COLLINS, M B, and MASSIE, K S (editors). (Amsterdam: Elsevier.)

McGEARY, S E, CHEADLE, M J, WARNER, M R, and BLUNDELL, D J, 1987. Crustal structure of the continental shelf around Britain derived from BIRPS deep seismic profiling. 33–41 in *Petroleum geology of North West Europe.* BROOKS, J, and GLENNIE, K W (editors). (London: Graham and Trotman.)

McLEAN, A C. 1978. Evolution of fault-controlled ensialic basins in northwestern Britain. 325–346 *in* Crustal evolution of northwestern Britain and adjacent regions. BOWES, D R, and LEAKE, B E (editors). *Geological Journal Special Issue,* No. 1.

— and DEEGAN, C E (editors). 1978. The solid geology of the Clyde sheet (55°N/6°W). *Report of the Institute of Geological Sciences,* No. 78/9.

— and WREN, A E. 1978. Gravity and magnetic studies of the lower Firth of Clyde. 7–27 *in* The solid geology of the Clyde sheet (55°N/6°W). McLEAN, A C, and DEEGAN, C E (editors). *Report of the Institute of Geological Sciences,* No. 78/9.

— — and WALKER, J H D. 1970. Gravity, magnetic and sparker surveys in the Firth of Clyde. *Proceedings of the Geologists' Association,* Vol. 166, 75–76.

McQUILLIN, R, BACON, M, and BINNS, P E. 1975. The Blackstones Tertiary igneous complex. *Scottish Journal of Geology,* Vol. 11, 179–92.

— and BINNS, P E. 1973. Geological structure of the Sea of the Hebrides. *Nature Physical Science, London,* Vol. 241, 2–4.

— and WATSON, J V. 1973. Large-scale basement structures of the Outer Hebrides in the light of geophysical evidence. *Nature Physical Science, London,* Vol. 245, 1–3.

McWHIRTER, N (editor). 1981. *Guinness book of records* (edition 27). (Enfield: Guinness Superlatives Limited.)

MITCHELL, J G, JONES, E J W, and JONES, G T. 1976. The composition and age of basalts dredged from the Blackstones igneous centre, western Scotland. *Geological Magazine,* Vol. 113, 525–533.

MORTON, A C, and five others. 1988. Early Tertiary volcanic rocks in well 163/6–1A, Rockall Trough. 293–308 *in* Early Tertiary volcanism and the opening of the NE Atlantic. MORTON, A C, and PARSON, L M (editors). *Special Publication of the Geological Society of London,* No. 39.

MORTON, N. 1983. Palaeocurrents and palaeo-environment of part of the Bearreraig Sandstone (Middle Jurassic) of Skye and Raasay, Inner Hebrides. *Scottish Journal of Geology,* Vol. 19, 87–95.

— 1987. Jurassic subsidence history in the Hebrides, NW Scotland. *Marine and Petroleum Geology,* Vol. 4, 226–242.

— 1989. Jurassic sequence stratigraphy in the Hebrides Basin, NW Scotland. *Marine and Petroleum Geology,* Vol. 6, 243–260.

— SMITH, R M, GOLDEN, M, and JAMES, A V. 1987. Comparative stratigraphic study of Triassic–Jurassic sedimentation and basin evolution in the northern North Sea and north-west of the British Isles. 697–709 in *Petroleum geology of North West Europe.* BROOKS, J, and GLENNIE, K W (editors). (London: Graham and Trotman.)

MUIR WOOD, R. 1989. Fifty million years of 'passive margin' deformation in north west Europe. 7–36 in *Earthquakes at North Atlantic passive margins: neotectonics and postglacial rebound.* GREGERSON, S, and BASHAM, P W (editors). (Dordrecht: Kluwer Academic Publishers.)

MUSSETT, A E, DAGLEY, P, and SKELHORN, R R. 1988. Time and duration of activity in the British Tertiary Igneous Province. 337–348 in Early Tertiary volcanism and the opening of the NE Atlantic. MORTON, A C, and PARSON, L M (editors). *Special Publication of the Geological Society of London,* No. 39.

MYKURA, W. 1960. The replacement of coal by limestone and the reddening of Coal Measures in the Ayrshire Coalfield. *Bulletin of the Geological Survey of Great Britain,* No. 16, 69–109.

— 1967. The Upper Carboniferous rocks of south-east Ayrshire. *Bulletin of the Geological Survey of Great Britain,* No. 26, 23–98.

— 1983. Old Red Sandstone. 205–252 in *The geology of Scotland* (2nd edition). CRAIG, G Y (editor). (Edinburgh: Scottish Academic Press.)

NICHOLSON, P G. 1991. North Western Britain (Hebridean Scotland): Mid to Late Proterozoic. *In* Atlas of palaeogeography and lithofacies. COPE, J C W, INGHAM, J K, and RAWSON, P F (editors). *Memoir of the Geological Society, of London,* No. 13.

NICHOLSON, R. 1978. The Camas Malag Formation: an interbedded rythmite/conglomerate sequence of probable Triassic age, Loch Slapin, Isle of Skye *Scottish Journal of Geology,* Vol. 14, 301–309.

OATES, M J. 1978. A revised stratigraphy for the western Scottish Lower Lias. *Proceedings of the Yorkshire Geological Society,* Vol. 42, 143–165.

OFOEGBU, C O, and BOTT, M H P. 1985. Interpretation of the Minch linear magnetic anomaly and of a similar feature on the shelf north of Lewis by non-linear optimisation. *Journal of the Geological Society of London,* Vol. 142, 1077–1087.

PANTIN, H M. 1991. The sea-bed sediments around the United Kingdom; their bathymetric and physical environment, grain size, mineral composition and associated bedforms. *British Geological Survey Research Report,* SB/90/1.

PARNELL, J, and MEIGHAN, I G. 1989. Lignite and associated deposits of the Tertiary Lough Neagh Basin, Northern Ireland. *Journal of the Geological Society of London,* Vol. 146, 351–352.

PATERSON, I B, and HALL, I H S. 1986. Lithostratigraphy of the late Devonian and early Carboniferous rocks in the Midland Valley of Scotland. *Report of the British Geological Survey,* Vol. 18, No. 3.

— — and STEPHENSON, D. 1990. Geology of the Greenock district. *Memoir of the British Geological Survey,* Sheets 30°W and 29°E (Scotland).

PEACH, B N, and HORNE, J. 1930. *Chapters on the geology of Scotland.* (London: Oxford University Press.)

PEACOCK, J D. 1981. Scottish late-glacial marine deposits and their environmental significance. 222–236 in *The Quaternary in Britain.* NEALE, J W, and HENLEY, J R (editors). (Oxford: Pergammon Press.)

— 1984. Quaternary Geology of the Outer Hebrides. *Report of the British Geological Survey,* Vol. 16, No. 2.

— GRAHAM, D K, ROBINSON, J E, and WILKINSON, I. 1977. Evolution and chronology of late glacial marine environments at Lochgilphead, Scotland. 89–100 in *Studies in the Scottish Lateglacial environment.* GRAY, J M, and LOWE, J J (editors). (Oxford: Pergamon Press.)

— HARKNESS, D D, HOUSLEY, R A, LITTLE, J A, and PAUL, M A. 1989. Radiocarbon ages for a glaciomarine bed associated with the maximum to the Loch Lomond Readvance in west Benderloch, Argyll. *Scottish Journal of Geology,* Vol. 25, 60–79.

PENDLEBURY, D C, and DOBSON, M R. 1976. Sediments and microfaunal distributions in the eastern Malin Sea, as determined by sidescan sonar and sampling. *Scottish Journal of Geology,* Vol. 11, 315–332.

PENN, I E, and MERRIMAN, R J. 1978. Jurassic (Toarcian to Bajocian) ammonites in the Shiant Isles, Outer Hebrides. *Scottish Journal of Geology,* Vol. 14, 45–53.

— and seven others. 1983. The Larne No. 2 borehole: discovery of a new Permian volcanic centre. *Scottish Journal of Geology,* Vol. 19, 333–346.

PHEMISTER, J. 1960. *British regional geology: the Northern Highlands* (3rd edition). (Edinburgh: HMSO for Institute of Geological Sciences.)

PIASECKI, M A J, and van BREEMAN, O. 1983. Field and isotopic evidence for a c. 750 Ma tectonothermal event in Moine rocks in the Central Highland region of the Scottish Caledonides. *Transactions of the Royal Society of Edinburgh: Earth Sciences,* Vol. 73, 119–134.

PIPER, D J W. 1970. Eolian sediments in the basal New Red Sandstone sediments of Arran. *Scottish Journal of Geology,* Vol. 6, 295–308.

PITCHER, W S. 1969. North-east trending faults of Scotland and Ireland and chronology of displacements. 723–773 in North Atlantic — geology and continental drift, a symposium. KAY, M (editor). *Memoir of the American Association of Petroleum Geologists,* No. 12.

— and BERGER, A R. 1972. *The geology of Donegal: a study of granite emplacement and unroofing.* (New York: Wiley-Interscience.)

PRESTON, J. 1963. The dolerite plug at Slemish, Co. Antrim, Ireland. *Liverpool and Manchester Geological Journal,* Vol. 3, 301–314.

— 1981. Tertiary igneous activity. 213–223 in *A geology of Ireland.* HOLLAND, C H (editor). (Edinburgh: Scottish Academic Press.)

PRINGLE, J. 1944. The Carboniferous rocks of Glas Eilean, Sound of Islay, Argyllshire. *Transactions of the Geological Society of Glasgow,* Vol. 20, 249–259.

— 1947. On the occurrence of Permian rocks in Islay and North Kintyre. *Transactions of the Edinburgh Geological Society,* Vol. 14, 297–301.

RICHEY, J E. 1961. *British regional geology: the Tertiary volcanic districts* (3rd edition). (Edinburgh: HMSO for Institute of Geological Sciences.)

RIDDIHOUGH, R P. 1968. Magnetic surveys off the north coast of Ireland. *Proceedings of the Royal Irish Acadamy,* Vol. 66B, 27–41.

— and YOUNG, D G G. 1971. Gravity and magnetic surveys of Inishowen and adjoining sea areas off the north coast of Ireland. *Proceedings of the Geological Society of London,* No. 1664, 215–220.

RITCHIE, W. 1975. *The beaches of Cowal, Bute and Arran.* (Aberdeen: University of Aberdeen.)

— and MATHER, A S. 1970. *The beaches of Lewis and Harris.* (Aberdeen: University of Aberdeen.)

ROBERTS, D G, BOTT, M H P, and URUSKI, C. 1983. Structure and origin of the Wyville–Thomson Ridge. 133–158 in *Structure and development of the Greenland–Scotland Ridge: new methods and concepts.* BOTT, M H P, SAXOV, S, TALWANI, M, and THIEDE, J (editors). (New York and London: Plenum Press.)

ROBERTS, J L. 1966 Ignimbrite eruptions in the volcanic history of the Glencoe cauldron subsidence. *Geological Journal,* Vol. 5, 173–184.

— and TREAGUS, J E. 1977. The Dalradian rocks of the South-west Highlands — introduction. *Scottish Journal of Geology,* Vol. 13, 87–99.

ROBINSON, J E. 1980. The marine ostracod record from the Lateglacial Period in Britain and NW Europe: a review. 115–122 in *Studies in the Lateglacial of North-West Europe.* LOWE, J J, GRAY, J M, and ROBINSON, J E (editors). (Oxford: Pergamon Press.)

ROBINSON, M, and BALLANTYNE, C K. 1979. Evidence for a glacial re-advance pre-dating the Loch Lomond Readvance in Wester Ross. *Scottish Journal of Geology,* Vol. 15, 271–277.

ROGERS, G, DEMPSTER, T J, BLUCK, B J, and TANNER, P W G. 1989. A high precision U-Pb age for the Ben Vuirich granite: implications for the evolution of the Scottish Dalradian Supergroup. *Journal of the Geological Society,* Vol. 146, 789–798.

RUDDIMAN, W F, SANCETTA, C D, and McINTYRE, A. 1977. Glacial/interglacial response rate of sub-polar North Atlantic waters to climatic change: the record in ocean sediments. *Philosophical Transactions of the Royal Society of London,* Vol. 280B, 119–142.

SAGER, G, and SAMMLER, R. 1975. *Atlas der Gezeitenströme für die Nordsee, den Kanal und die Irische See.* (Rostock: Hydrographischer Dienst der Deutchen Demokratischen Republik.) [In German.]

SCRUTTON, R A. 1986. The geology, crustal structure and evolution of the Rockall Trough and Faeroe–Shetland Channel. *Proceedings of the Royal Society of Edinburgh,* Vol. 88B, 7–26.

SEARLE, A. 1989. Sedimentology and early diagenesis of the Lower Jurassic, Applecross, Wester Ross. *Scottish Journal of Geology,* Vol. 25, 45–62.

SELBY, I C. 1987. Glaciated shorelines on Barra and Vatersay. *Quaternary Newsletter,* Vol. 53, 16–22.

SEVASTOPULO, G D. 1981. Lower Carboniferous. 146–161 in *A geology of Ireland.* HOLLAND, C H (editor). (Edinburgh: Scottish Academic Press.)

SHENNAN, I. 1989. Holocene crustal movements and sea-level changes in Great Britain. *Journal of Quaternary Science,* Vol. 4, 77–89.

SHOTTON, F W, BLUNDELL, D J, and WILLIAMS, R E G. 1970. Birmingham University Radiocarbon Dates IV. *Radiocarbon,* Vol. 12, 385–399.

SISSONS, J B. 1964. The Perth Readvance in central Scotland, Part II. *Scottish Geographical Magazine,* Vol. 80, 28–36.

— 1981. The last Scottish ice sheet: facts and speculative discussion. *Boreas,* Vol. 10, 1–17.

— and CORNISH, R. 1982. Differential glacio-isostatic uplift of crustal blocks at Glen Roy, Scotland. *Quaternary Research,* Vol. 18, 268–288.

SMITH, C G. 1989. Scottish Highlands and Southern Uplands Mineral Portfolio: silica sand and silica rock sources. *British Geological Survey Technical Report,* WF/89/6.

SMITH, P J, and BOTT, M H P. 1975. Structure of the crust beneath the Caledonian foreland and Caledonian belt of the north Scottish shelf region. *Geophysical Journal of the Royal Astronomical Society,* Vol. 40, 187–205.

SMYTHE, D K. 1989. Rockall Trough — Cretaceous or Late Palaeozoic? *Scottish Journal of Geology,* Vol. 25, 5–43.

— and KENOLTY, N. 1975. Tertiary sediments in the Sea of the Hebrides. *Journal of the Geological Society of London,* Vol. 131, 227–233.

— SOWERBUTTS, W T C, BACON, M, and McQUILLIN R. 1972. Deep sedimentary basin below northern Skye and the Little Minch. *Nature Physical Science, London,* Vol. 236, 87–89.

— and six others. 1982. Deep structure of the Caledonides revealed by the MOIST reflection profile. *Nature, London,* Vol. 229, 338–340.

SNELLING, N J (editor). 1987. The chronology of the geological record. *Memoir of the Geological Society of London,* No. 10.

SNYDER, D B, and FLACK, C A. 1990. A Caledonian age for reflectors within the mantle lithosphere north and west of Scotland. *Tectonics,* Vol. 9, 903–922.

SPEIGHT, J M, and MITCHELL, J G. 1978. The Permo-Carboniferous dyke-swarm of northern Argyll and its bearing on dextral displacement on the Great Glen Fault. *Journal of the Geological Society of London,* Vol. 136, 3–11.

SPENCER, A M. 1971. Late Pre-Cambrian glaciation in Scotland. *Memoir of the Geological Society of London,* No. 6.

STEEL, R J. 1971a. New Red Sandstone movement on the Minch Fault. *Nature Physical Science, London,* Vol. 234, 158–159.

— 1971b. Sedimentation of the New Red Sandstone in the Hebridean province, Scotland. Unpublished PhD thesis, University of Glasgow.

— 1974a. New Red Sandstone floodplain and piedmont sedimentation in the Hebridean province, Scotland. *Journal of Sedimentary Petrology,* Vol. 44, 328–357.

— 1974b. Cornstone (fossil caliche) — its origin, stratigraphic and sedimentological importance in the New Red Sandstone, western Scotland. *Journal of Geology,* Vol. 82, 351–369.

— 1977. Triassic rift basins of northwest Scotland — their configuration, infilling and development. 7/1–7/18 in *Proceedings of the Northern North Sea Symposium.* FINSTAD, K G, and SELLEY, R C (editors). (Oslo: Norwegian Petroleum Society.)

— and WILSON, A C. 1975. Sedimentation and tectonism (? Permo-Triassic) on the margin of the North Minch Basin, Lewis. *Journal of the Geological Society of London,* Vol. 131, 183–202.

STEERS, J A. 1973. *The coastline of Scotland.* (Cambridge: Cambridge University Press.)

STEIN, A M. 1988. Basement controls upon basin development in the Caledonian foreland, NW Scotland. *Basin Research,* Vol. 1, 107–119.

STEPHENS, N, and McCABE, A M. 1977. Late-Pleistocene ice movements and patterns of Late- and Post-Glacial shorelines on the coast of Ulster, Ireland. 179–198 in *The Quaternary history of the Irish Sea.* KIDSON, C, and TOOLEY, M J (editors). (Liverpool: Seel House Press.)

— and SYNGE, F M. 1965. Late-Pleistocene shorelines and drift limits in north Donegal. *Proceedings of the Royal Irish Academy,* Series B, Vol. 64, 131–153.

STEVENS, A. 1914. Notes on the geology of the Stornoway district of Lewis. *Transactions of the Geological Society of Glasgow,* Vol. 15, 51.

STEWART, A D. 1969. Torridonian rocks of Scotland reviewed. 595–608 *in* North Atlantic — geology and continental drift, a symposium. KAY, M (editor). *Memoir of the American Association of Petroleum Geologists,* No. 12.

— 1975. 'Torridonian' rocks of western Scotland. 43–51 *in* Precambrian. HARRIS, A L, and five others (editors). *Special Publication of the Geological Society of London,* No. 6.

— 1988. The Stoer Group, Scotland. 97–112 in *Later Proterozoic stratigraphy of the Northern Atlantic regions.* WINCHESTER, J A (editor). (Glasgow: Blackie.)

— and HACKMAN, B D. 1973. Precambrian sediments of western Islay. *Scottish Journal of Geology,* Vol. 9, 185–201.

STOKER, M S. 1982. Old Red Sandstone sedimentation and deformation in the Great Glen fault zone, NW of Loch Linnhe. *Scottish Journal of Geology,* Vol. 18, 147–166.

— LONG, D, and FYFE, J A. 1985. A revised Quaternary stratigraphy for the central North Sea. *Report of the British Geological Survey,* Vol. 17, No. 2.

— and five others. 1988. Early Tertiary basalts and tuffaceous sandstones from the Hebrides Shelf and Wyville–Thomson Ridge, NE Atlantic. 271–282 *in* Early Tertiary volcanism and the opening of the NE Atlantic. MORTON, A C, and PARSON L M (editors). *Special Publication of the Geological Society of London,* No. 39.

— and others. In press. *United Kingdom offshore regional report: the geology of the Hebrides and west Shetland shelves, and adjacent deep-water areas.* (London: HMSO for the British Geological Survey.)

STONE, P, FLOYD, J D, BARNES, R P, and LINTERN, B C. 1987. A sequential back-arc and foreland basin thrust duplex model for the

Southern Uplands of Scotland. *Journal of the Geological Society of London,* Vol. 144, 753–764.

STORETVEDT, K M, and STEEL, R J. 1977. Palaeomagnetic evidence for the age of the Stornoway Formation. *Scottish Journal of Geology,* Vol, 13, 263–269.

SUTHERLAND, D G. 1981a. The high-level marine shell beds of Scotland and the build-up of the last Scottish ice sheet. *Boreas,* Vol. 10, 247–254.

— 1981b. The raised shorelines and deglaciation of the Loch Long/Loch Fyne area, western Scotland. Unpublished PhD thesis, University of Edinburgh.

— 1984. The Quaternary deposits and landforms of Scotland and the neighbouring shelves: a review. *Quaternary Science Reviews,* Vol. 3, 157–254.

— and WALKER, M J C. 1984. A late Devensian ice-free area and possible interglacial site on the Isle of Lewis, Scotland. *Nature, London,* Vol. 309, 701–703.

SUTHERLAND, D S (editor). 1982. *Igneous rocks of the British Isles.* (Chichester: John Wiley and Sons.)

SUTTON, J, and WATSON, J V. 1964. Some aspects of 'Torridonian' stratigraphy in Skye. *Proceedings of the Geologists' Association,* Vol. 75, 251–289.

TATE, M P, and DOBSON, M R. 1989. Late Permian to early Mesozoic rifting and sedimentation offshore NW Ireland. *Marine and Petroleum Geology,* Vol. 6, 49–59.

THOMAS, B W, MILLER, J M, and MALCOLM, A. 1984. Radiometric surveys of the seabed. *Proceedings of the Oceanology International '84 Conference, Brighton,* Vol. 1, Paper No. 10, 11.

TORSVIK, T H, and STURT, B A. 1987. On the origin and stability of remnance and the magnetic fabric of the Torridonian Red Beds, NW Scotland. *Scottish Journal of Geology,* Vol. 23, 23–38.

TRUEBLOOD, S, and MORTON, N. 1991. Comparative sequence stratigraphy and structural styles of the Slyne Trough and Hebrides Basin. *Journal of the Geological Society of London,* Vol. 148, 197–202.

UPTON, B G J. 1982. Carboniferous to Permian volcanism in the stable foreland. 255–275 in *Igneous rocks of the British Isles.* SUTHERLAND, D S (editor). (Chichester: John Wiley and Sons.)

— 1988. History of Tertiary igneous activity in the North Atlantic borderlands. 429–454 *in* Early Tertiary volcanism and the opening of the NE Atlantic. MORTON, A C, and PARSON, L M (editors). S*pecial Publication of the Geological Society of London,* No. 39.

— FITTON, J G and MACINTYRE, R M. 1987. The Glas Eilean lavas: evidence of a Lower Permian volcano-tectonic basin between Islay and Jura, Inner Hebrides. *Transactions of the Royal Society of Edinburgh: Earth Sciences,* Vol. 77, 289–293.

VAIL, P R, and TODD, R G. 1981. Northern North Sea Jurassic unconformities chronostratigraphy and sea level changes from seismic stratigraphy. 216–235 in *Petroleum geology of the continental shelf of North-West Europe.* ILLING, L V, and HOBSON, G D (editors). (London: Heyden and Son.)

WAGER, L R, and BROWN, G M. 1968. *Layered igneous rocks.* (Edinburgh: Oliver and Boyd.)

WALKER, F. 1930. The geology of the Shiant Isles (Hebrides). *Quarterly Journal of the Geological Society of London,* Vol. 86, 355–398.

— 1959. The Islay–Jura dyke swarm. *Transactions of the Geological Society of Glasgow,* Vol. 24, 121–137.

WALKER, M J C, BALLANTYNE, C K, LOWE, J J, and SUTHERLAND, D G. 1988. A reinterpretation of the Lateglacial environmental history of the Isle of Skye, Inner Hebrides, Scotland. *Journal of Quaternary Science,* Vol. 3, 135–146.

WARRINGTON, G. 1981. The indigenous micropalaeontology of British Triassic shelf sea deposits. 61–70 in *Microfossils from Recent and fossil shelf seas.* NEALE, J W, and BRASIER, M D (editors). (Chichester: Ellis Horwood Ltd.)

— and eight others. 1980. A correlation of Triassic rocks in the British Isles. *Special Report of the Geological Society of London,* No. 13.

— and IVIMEY-COOK, H C. 1990. Biostratigraphy of the late Triassic and early Jurassic: a review of type sections in southern Britain. *Les Cahiers de l'Université Catholique de Lyon,* No. 3, 207–213.

WATSON, J V. 1975. The Lewisian Complex. 15–29 in Precambrian. HARRIS, A L, and five others (editors). *Special Report of the Geological Society of London,* No. 6.

— 1977. The Outer Hebrides: a geological perspective. *Proceedings of the Geologists' Association,* Vol. 88, 1–14.

— 1983. Lewisian. 23–48 in *The geology of Scotland* (2nd edition). CRAIG, G Y (editor). (Edinburgh: Scottish Academic Press.)

WESTBROOK, G K, and BORRADAILE, G J. 1978. The geological significance of magnetic anomalies in the Islay region. *Scottish Journal of Geology,* Vol. 14, 213–224.

WEYMARN, J von, and EDWARDS, K J. 1973. Interstadial site on the island of Lewis, Scotland. *Nature, London,* Vol. 246, 473–474.

WHITTAKER, T J T. 1991. Shoreline wave power on the Isle of Islay. *Underwater Technology,* Vol. 17, 9–15.

WILKINSON, G C, BAZLEY, R A B, and BOULTER, M C. 1980. The geology and palynology of the Oligocene Lough Neagh Clays, Northern Ireland. *Journal of the Geological Society of London ,*Vol. 137, 65–75.

WILKINSON, S B. 1907. The geology of Islay, including Oronsay and portions of Colonsay and Jura. *Memoir of the Geological Survey of Scotland.*

WILLIAMS, G E. 1968. 'Torridonian' weathering, and its bearing on 'Torridonian' palaeoclimate and source. *Scottish Journal of Geology,* Vol. 4, 164–187.

— 1969. Characteristics and origin of a Precambrian pediment. *Journal of Geology,* Vol. 77, 183–207.

WILSON, V, and FLETT, J S. 1921. The lead, zinc, copper and nickel ores of Scotland. *Memoir of the Geological Survey, Special Report on the Mineral Resources of Great Britain.*

WILSON, H E. 1972. *British regional geology: Northern Ireland.* (Belfast: HMSO for Geological Survey of Northern Ireland.)

— 1981. Permian and Mesozoic. 201– 212 in *A geology of Ireland.* HOLLAND, C H (editor). (Edinburgh: Scottish Academic Press.)

— and MANNING, P I. 1978. Geology of the Causeway coast. *Memoir of the Geological Survey of Northern Ireland,* Sheet 7 (N. Ireland).

WOOD, M V, HALL, J, and DOODY, J J. 1988. Distribution of early Tertiary lavas in the NE Rockall Trough. 283–292 *in* Early Tertiary volcanism and the opening of the NE Atlantic. MORTON, A C, and PARSON, L M (editors). *Special Report of the Geological Society of London,* No. 39.

— — and VAN HOORN, B. 1987. Post-Mesozoic differential subsidence in the north-east Rockall Trough related to volcanicity and sedimentation. 677–685 in *Petroleum geology of North West Europe.* BROOKS, J, and GLENNIE, K W (editors). (London: Graham and Trotman.)

WOOLLEY, A R, and JERMY, A C. 1978. Geology. 4.1–4.25 in *The island of Mull; a survey of its flora and environment.* JERMY, A C, and CRABBE, J A (editors). Vol. 25. (London: British Museum.)

YOUNG, J, and CRAIG, R. 1871. Notes on the occurrence of seeds of fresh-water plants and arctic shells along with the remains of the mammoth and reindeer in beds under the boulder clay of Kilmaurs. *Transactions of the Geological Society of Glasgow,* Vol. 3, 310–321.

ZIEGLER, P A. 1981. Evolution of sedimentary basins in North-West Europe. 3–39 in *Petroleum geology of the continental shelf of North-West Europe.* ILLING, L V, and HOBSON, G D (editors). (London: Heyden and Son.)

— 1988. Evolution of the Arctic–North Atlantic and the western Tethys. *Memoir of the American Association of Petroleum Geologists,* No. 43.

INDEX

BRITISH GEOLOGICAL SURVEY

Keyworth, Nottingham NG12 5GG
(0602) 363100

Murchison House, West Mains Road, Edinburgh EH9 3LA
031-667 1000

London Information Office, Natural History Museum
Earth Galleries, Exhibition Road, London SW7 2DE
071 589 4090

The full range of Survey publications is available through the
Sales Desks at Keyworth and at Murchison House,
Edinburgh, and in the BGS London Information Office in
the Natural History Museum Earth Galleries. The adjacent
bookshop stocks the more popular books for sale over the
counter. Most BGS books and reports are listed in HMSO's
Sectional List 45, and can be bought from HMSO and
through HMSO agents and retailers. Maps are listed in the
BGS Map Catalogue, and can be bought from Ordnance
Survey agents as well as from BGS.

*The British Geological Survey carries out the geological survey of
Great Britain and Northern Ireland (the latter as an agency
service for the government of Northern Ireland), and of the
surrounding continental shelf, as well as its basic research
projects. It also undertakes programmes of British technical aid
in geology in developing countries as arranged by the Overseas
Development Administration.*

*The British Geological Survey is a component body of the
Natural Environment Research Council.*

HMSO publications are available from:

HMSO Publications Centre
(Mail, fax and telephone orders only)
PO Box 276, London, SW8 5DT
Telephone orders 071-873 9090
General enquiries 071-873 0011
Queuing system in operation for both numbers
Fax orders 071-873 8200

HMSO Bookshops
49 High Holborn, London, WC1V 6HB
(Counter service only)
071-873 0011 Fax 071-873 8200
258 Broad Street, Birmingham, B1 2HE
021-643 3740 Fax 021-643 6510
33 Wine Street, Bristol, BS1 2BQ
0272 264306 Fax 0272 294515
9-21 Princess Street, Manchester, M60 8AS
061-834 7201 Fax 061-833 0634
16 Arthur Street, Belfast, BT1 4GD
0232 238451 Fax 0232 235401
71 Lothian Road, Edinburgh, EH3 9AZ
031-228 4181 Fax 031-229 2734

HMSO's Accredited Agents
(see Yellow Pages)

And through good booksellers

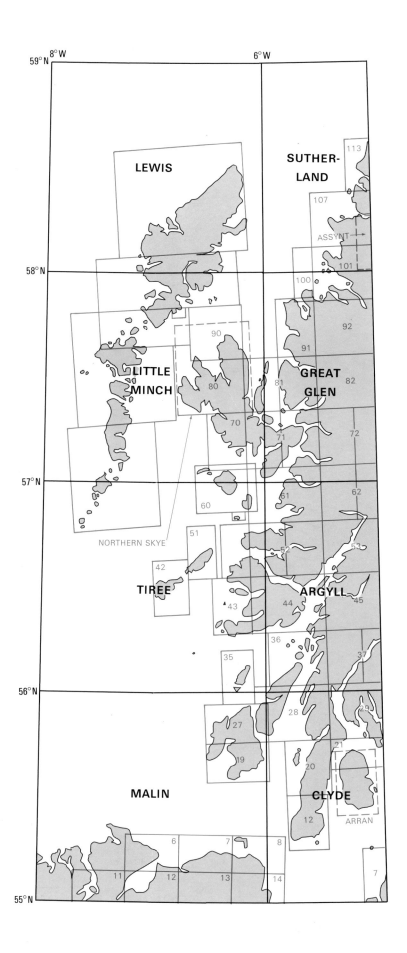

59°N 8°W

6°W

LEWIS

SUTHER-
LAND

113

107

ASSYNT

58°N

101

100

LITTLE
MINCH

90

92

91

80

81

GREAT
GLEN

82

70

72

71

NORTHERN SKYE

57°N

61

62

60

51

52

53

42

TIREE

43

44

ARGYLL

45

36

37

35

56°N

28

29

27

21

19

20

MALIN

CLYDE

12

ARRAN

6

7

8

7

11

12

13

14

55°N